D0909649

PROPOSITIONAL CALCULUS

MONOGRAPHS IN MODERN LOGIC

edited by

G. B. KEENE

The Development of Mathematical Logic	P. H. Nidditch
Axiomatics	Robert Blanché
Propositional Calculus	P. H. Nidditch
Truth-Functional Logic	J. A. Faris
Quantification Theory	J. A. Faris
First-Order Functional Calculus	G. B. Keene
The Logic of Commands	Nicholas Rescher

PROPOSITIONAL CALCULUS

BY

P. H. Nidditch

LONDON: Routledge & Kegan Paul Ltd
NEW YORK: Dover Publications Inc.

First published 1962
by Routledge & Kegan Paul Ltd
Broadway House, 68-74 *Carter Lane*
*London, E.C.*4

Second impression 1965

Published in the United States of America by
Dover Publications Inc.
180 *Varick Street*
New York, 10014

Printed in Great Britain
by Latimer, Trend & Co. Ltd., Plymouth

CONTENTS

PREFACE

The propositional calculus is the formal logic of statement connections, statement connections being notions expressed by certain uses of words like 'not', 'or', 'and', and 'implies'. Such notions play an essential part in the making of inferences.

The propositional calculus is called a *calculus* because it is an abstract theory developed in a purely formal way. Theorems in it are formulae deducible by virtue of explicitly stated rules from initially accepted formulae. The initially accepted formulae represent principles of the logic of statement connections, and the rules of deduction are so constructed as to allow the derivation of only those formulae which are also such principles. One criterion for a formula to be a principle in this field is given by the method of valuation or so-called 'truth' tables, which the reader might be already familiar with. (The essentials of the method are expounded in Ch. 11.) The criterion is that a formula represents a principle if and only if it is tautologous, in the technical sense of 'tautologous' defined with respect to the valuation method.

The propositional calculus is a basic part of logic; other parts build upon it and are extensions of it.

In addition to drawing deductions from the postulates of a propositional calculus system, it is important to consider the axiomatics of the system. One should inquire into its consistency: is it free from contradiction? One should inquire into the independence of its postulates: are any of them redundant, being deducible from the others? One should inquire into its completeness: is every principle of the logic of statement connections provable in the system? In modern logic most of the interest is concentrated on the axiomatics of individual systems and of types of system. The final part of the present work (pages 60–81) is devoted to substantiating the answers to be given to the chief questions of the axiomatics of the system developed here.

There is not just one system of the propositional calculus; many have been devised. One reason for choosing the system adopted here is its being rather different from those which are to be found in available current texts. At the same time, the fundamental techniques are the same for all the systems; therefore, having mastered the present one, the reader will have little difficulty in dealing with others.

Chapter One

FORMULAE

The system of the propositional calculus that will be developed in this monograph will be referred to as *P*.

There are three and only three kinds of symbol in *P* itself:

(i) p, q, r, s and these same letters with positive integer subscripts, as $p_1, p_2, p_3, \ldots$ A symbol of this kind is called a *propositional variable*.

(ii) $-, \vee, \&, \rightarrow$. These four symbols denote respectively certain concepts of negation, disjunction, conjunction, and implication. A symbol of this kind is called a *connective*.

(iii) (,). A symbol of this kind is called a *parenthesis*, the former being called a *left-hand*, and the latter a *right-hand*, parenthesis.

Any symbol belonging to (i), (ii), or (iii) will be called a *P*-symbol.

(1) $((-s \;\&\; r) \rightarrow (p \vee q_2))$

and

(2) $(p) - \vee\; s \;\&(\rightarrow q_2(\;)r)$

are finite linear sequences of *P*-symbols. The class of all such sequences is divided into two mutually exclusive sub-classes. One sub-class contains all those sequences which are, so to speak, the grammatically correct sentences of *P*, sequences that are called the *well-formed formulae*, or more briefly the *formulae*, of *P*; (1) is an example of a formula. The other sub-class contains all the finite linear sequences that are not formulae; (2) is an example of such a sequence. We shall be interested henceforth only in sequences that are formulae.

In defining which finite linear sequences of *P*-symbols are formulae, and throughout what follows, we use the letters A, B, C, D, E as *names* of any formulae at all; we shall later use also, for the same purpose, these letters with positive integer subscripts or with integer variables such as i, j, and n. These names are not, of course, symbols in the calculus *P* itself; they belong to the languages used for speaking *about P*, not for speaking *in P*.

Definition 1. (*a*) A propositional variable is a formula. (*b*) If A is a formula, then $-A$ is a formula. (*c*) If A and B are formulae, then $(A \vee B)$, $(A \,\&\, B)$, and $(A \rightarrow B)$ are formulae. (*d*) The only formulae are those specified to be such by (*a*), (*b*), or (*c*).

(3) $(-p \,\&\, (q \rightarrow p))$

is a formula because, by (*a*) of Definition 1, p and q are formulae, so $-p$ is a formula by (*b*) and $(q \rightarrow p)$ is a formula by (*c*), and thus, by (*c*) again, (3) is a formula.

The requirement, in Definition 1 (*c*), of a pair of parentheses to surround $A \vee B$, $A \,\&\, B$, $A \rightarrow B$, is motivated chiefly by the wish to avoid ambiguity in the reading of an expression. Consider, for example,

(4) $p \,\&\, q \rightarrow r \rightarrow s$.

It is impossible to determine how this expression is built up. There are five possible readings, which can be fixed by the insertion of parentheses:

(5) $(((p \,\&\, q) \rightarrow r) \rightarrow s)$;
(6) $((p \,\&\, q) \rightarrow (r \rightarrow s))$;
(7) $((p \,\&\, (q \rightarrow r)) \rightarrow s)$;
(8) $(p \,\&\, ((q \rightarrow r) \rightarrow s))$;
(9) $(p \,\&\, (q \rightarrow (r \rightarrow s)))$.

In practice, however, the use of parentheses required by Definition 1 (*c*) is modified by adopting certain conventions which effect a large reduction in the number of parentheses employed—though, when such conventions are adopted and applied, the resulting finite linear sequences of *P*-symbols are not, as they stand, formulae of *P* but are shorthand expressions for such formulae. One convention is that the outermost pair of parentheses of a whole formula may be omitted. Another is that, in the absence of restricting parentheses, the connectives have the following order of priority: $-$ precedes the others, $\&$ precedes $\vee$ and $\rightarrow$, while $\vee$ precedes $\rightarrow$. A third convention is to write the negation sign as a bar over the formula (or shorthand expression for the formula) to be negated, this bar, called a *vinculum*, having a parenthetical function also. For example,

(10) $\bar{p} \,\&\, q \vee r \rightarrow s$

may be written instead of

(11) $(((-p \,\&\, q) \vee r) \rightarrow s)$,

and

(12) $p \,\&\, \bar{q} \vee p \,\&\, \bar{r} \rightarrow p \;\; \& \, \overline{q \,\&\, r}$

may be written instead of

(13) $(((p \,\&\!- q) \vee (p \,\&\!- r)) \rightarrow (p \,\&\!-(q \,\&\, r)))$.

We shall henceforth adopt the three conventions mentioned and shall, for the sake of convenient brevity, regard the expressions resulting from their use as formulae.

Chapter Two

SUBSTITUTION

Let us begin the examination of the notion of substituting a formula C in the place of a propositional variable in a formula A by considering an example. Suppose A is $p \rightarrow (q \rightarrow p)$ and C is $\bar{r}$. If C is substituted for p throughout A, one obtains $\bar{r} \rightarrow (q \rightarrow \bar{r})$. A notation for this latter formula, which indicates how it has been or may be obtained, is $S_p^{\bar{r}}(p \rightarrow (q \rightarrow p))$.

It is intuitively obvious that the substitution of a formula C for each occurrence of a propositional variable in a formula A yields again a formula, which is similar in form to A. But, although the assertion is thus obvious, it is, strictly, in need of proof, and until the proof has been given it is illegitimate to define the result of substituting C for say p in A as 'the formula' which is identical with A except that each occurrence of p in A is made an occurrence of C. Because of this circumstance, we here define the operation of substitution in a somewhat different way, which guarantees that the result of a substitution is itself a formula. However, before giving this definition as a whole, we shall expound its individual clauses separately.

Let D and E designate propositional variables only, so that these letters stand in the present context for formulae such as p, q, and r, and not for any more complex formulae. (*a*) If A is D, then $S_D^C(A)$ is C. For example, $S^{q \vee r}_p(p)$ is $q \vee r$. (*b*) If A is D and E designates a propositional variable different from that designated by D, then $S^C_E(A)$ is D. For example, $S^{\bar{r}}_q(p)$ is p. (*c*) If $S^C_D(A)$ has been defined, then $S^C_D(\bar{A})$ is $\overline{S^C_D(A)}$. For example, $S^{q \to r}_p(\bar{p})$ is $\overline{q \to r}$. (*d*) If $S^C_D(A)$ and $S^C_D(B)$ have been defined, then $S^C_D(A \vee B)$ is $S^C_D(A) \vee S^C_D(B)$, $S^C_D(A \,\&\, B)$ is $S^C_D(A) \,\&\, S^C_D(B)$, and $S^C_D(A \to B)$ is $S^C_D(A) \to S^C_D(B)$. For example,

(1) $S^{q \to r}_p((p \to q) \,\&\, (p \vee r))$

is

(2) $((q \to r) \to q) \,\&\, ((q \to r) \vee r)$;

and

(3) $S^{\overline{q \vee r}}_q(\bar{q} \vee \overline{q \to p})$

is

(4) $\overline{S^{\overline{q \vee r}}_q(q)} \vee \overline{S^{\overline{q \vee r}}_q(q) \to S^{\overline{q \vee r}}_q(p)}$,

and so, explicitly, is

(5) $\overline{\overline{q \vee r}} \vee \overline{\overline{q \vee r} \to p}$.

Definition 2. Let D and E designate propositional variables. (*a*) If A is D, then $S^C_D(A)$ is C. (*b*) If D and E designate different propositional variables from one another and A is D, then $S^C_E(A)$ is A. (*c*) If $S^C_D(A)$ has been defined, then $S^C_D(\bar{A})$ is $\overline{S^C_D(A)}$. (*d*) If $S^C_D(A)$ and $S^C_D(B)$ have been defined, then $S^C_D(A \vee B)$ is $S^C_D(A) \vee S^C_D(B)$, $S^C_D(A \,\&\, B)$ is $S^C_D(A) \,\&\, S^C_D(B)$, and $S^C_D(A \to B)$ is $S^C_D(A) \to S^C_D(B)$.

Since, if A is any formula, and D_1 and D_2 are any propositional variables, $S^C_{D_1}(A)$ has been defined as itself a formula, it is permissible to consider such expressions for formulae as $S^{C_1}_{D_1}(S^{C_2}_{D_2}(A))$. This expression represents the formula obtainable by firstly substituting C_2 for D_2 in A and secondly substituting C_1 for D_1 in the formula got by performing the first substitution. The order of the substitutions is important: $S^{C_2}_{D_2}(S^{C_1}_{D_1}(A))$ is not necessarily the same formula as $S^{C_1}_{D_1}(S^{C_2}_{D_2}(A))$. For example,

(6) $S^{\bar{p}}_{p}(S^{p}_{q}(p \vee q \rightarrow q \vee p))$

is $S^{\bar{p}}_{p}(p \vee p \rightarrow p \vee p)$, which is turn is $\bar{p} \vee \bar{p} \rightarrow \bar{p} \vee \bar{p}$. On the other hand,

(7) $S^{p}_{q}(S^{\bar{p}}_{p}(p \vee q \rightarrow q \vee p))$

is $S^{p}_{q}(\bar{p} \vee q \rightarrow q \vee \bar{p})$, which in turn is $\bar{p} \vee p \rightarrow p \vee \bar{p}$.

Chapter Three

AXIOMS AND RULES OF DEDUCTION

The normal theoretical purpose of constructing a propositional calculus is to have a system which incorporates valid and only valid logical principles of the connectives. One chooses as starting-points a certain number of such principles, deducing other principles of connectives by use of these starting-points. The starting-points of *P* fall into two groups, one consisting of axioms, the other of rules of deduction, the latter enabling us to pass from premisses to conclusions. The axioms of *P* are eleven in number. All involve implication. The first two involve no other connectives. The next three involve disjunction, the following three conjunction, and the final three negation. It will be shown later (Ch. 12) that the axioms of P are mutually independent, so that if any were eliminated, the system would be the poorer: there would be at least one valid logical principle of connectives that would be unprovable in *P*. It will also be shown later (Ch. 13), by employing the notion of truth-table tautology as the criterion of validity, that every valid logical principle of connectives is provable in *P*; hence the starting-points of *P* are adequate.

The axioms of *P* are:

I. $p \rightarrow (q \rightarrow p)$;

II. $(p \rightarrow (q \rightarrow r)) \rightarrow ((p \rightarrow q) \rightarrow (p \rightarrow r))$;

III. $p \to p \vee q$;
IV. $q \to p \vee q$;
V. $(p \to r) \to ((q \to r) \to (p \vee q \to r))$;
VI. $p \,\&\, q \to p$;
VII. $p \,\&\, q \to q$;
VIII. $(r \to p) \to ((r \to q) \to (r \to p \,\&\, q))$;
IX. $(p \to q) \to (\bar{q} \to \bar{p})$;
X. $p \to \bar{\bar{p}}$;
XI. $\bar{\bar{p}} \to p$.

We now define which formulae are provable in P, the second and third clauses of our definition embodying the two rules of deduction of P, the former being the rule of substitution and the latter the rule of *modus ponens*. A formula that is provable in a system is often said to be a *true* formula of the system. This terminology will not be employed here.

Definition 3. (*a*) If A is an axiom, then A is provable. (*b*) If A is provable, then, D being a propositional variable, $S_D^C(A)$ is provable. (*c*) If A and $A \to B$ are provable, then B is provable. (*d*) The only provable formulae are those specified to be such by (*a*), (*b*), or (*c*).

We shall denote by V any provable formula.

Chapter Four

EXAMPLES OF PROVABLE FORMULAE

Theorem 1. $p \rightarrow V$ is provable.

Proof: 1. $p \rightarrow (q \rightarrow p)$
2. $V \rightarrow (q \rightarrow V)$
3. $V \rightarrow (D \rightarrow V)$
4. V
5. $D \rightarrow V$
6. $p \rightarrow V$.

In this proof, 1 is axiom I, 2 is obtained from 1 by substituting V for p, 3 is obtained from 2 by substituting D (a propositional variable with no occurences in V) for q, 4 is provable (by notational definition), 5 is obtained from 3 and 4 by *modus ponens*, and 6 is obtained from 5 by substituting p for D. With readily understood notations, 2 is $S_p^V(1)$, 3 is $S_q^D(2)$, 5 is 3, 4, mp, and 6 is S_D^p (5).

Theorem 2. $p \rightarrow p$ is provable.

Proof: 1. $(p \rightarrow (q \rightarrow r)) \rightarrow ((p \rightarrow q) \rightarrow (p \rightarrow r))$
2. $(p \rightarrow (q \rightarrow p)) \rightarrow ((p \rightarrow q) \rightarrow (p \rightarrow p))$
3. $p \rightarrow (q \rightarrow p)$
4. $(p \rightarrow q) \rightarrow (p \rightarrow p)$
5. $(p \rightarrow V) \rightarrow (p \rightarrow p)$
6. $p \rightarrow V$
7. $p \rightarrow p$.

In this proof, 1 is axiom II, 2 is $S_r^p(1)$, 3 is axiom I, 4 is 2, 3, mp, 5 is $S_p^{V}(4)$, 6 is Theorem 1, and 7 is 5, 6, mp.

Theorem 3. $p \vee q \rightarrow q \vee p$ is provable.

Proof:
1. $(p \rightarrow r) \rightarrow ((q \rightarrow r) \rightarrow (p \vee q \rightarrow r))$
2. $(p \rightarrow q \vee p) \rightarrow ((q \rightarrow q \vee p) \rightarrow (p \vee q \rightarrow q \vee p))$
3. $q \rightarrow p \vee q$
4. $q \rightarrow r \vee q$
5. $p \rightarrow r \vee p$
6. $p \rightarrow q \vee p$
7. $(q \rightarrow q \vee p) \rightarrow (p \vee q \rightarrow q \vee p)$
8. $p \rightarrow p \vee q$
9. $p \rightarrow p \vee r$
10. $q \rightarrow q \vee r$
11. $q \rightarrow q \vee p$
12. $p \vee q \rightarrow q \vee p$.

In this proof, 1 is axiom V, 2 is $S_r^{q \vee p}(1)$, 3 is axiom IV, 4 is $S_p^r(3)$, 5 is $S_q^p(4)$, 6 is $S_r^q(5)$, 7 is 2, 6, mp, 8 is axiom III, 9 is $S_q^r(8)$, 10 is $S_p^q(9)$, 11 is $S_r^p(10)$, and 12 is 7, 11, mp.

Theorem 4. $q \,\&\, p \rightarrow p \,\&\, q$ is provable.

Proof:
1. $(r \rightarrow p) \rightarrow ((r \rightarrow q) \rightarrow (r \rightarrow p \,\&\, q))$
2. $(q \,\&\, p \rightarrow p) \rightarrow ((q \,\&\, p \rightarrow q) \rightarrow (q \,\&\, p \rightarrow p \,\&\, q))$
3. $p \,\&\, q \rightarrow q$
4. $r \,\&\, q \rightarrow q$
5. $r \,\&\, p \rightarrow p$
6. $q \,\&\, p \rightarrow p$
7. $(q \,\&\, p \rightarrow q) \rightarrow (q \,\&\, p \rightarrow p \,\&\, q)$
8. $p \,\&\, q \rightarrow p$
9. $p \,\&\, r \rightarrow p$
10. $q \,\&\, r \rightarrow q$
11. $q \,\&\, p \rightarrow q$
12. $q \,\&\, p \rightarrow p \,\&\, q$.

In this proof, 1 is axiom VIII, 2 is $S_r^{q \,\&\, p}(1)$, 3 is axiom VII, 4 is $S^r_p(3)$, 5 is $S^p_q(4)$, 6 is $S^q_r(5)$, 7 is 2, 6, mp, 8 is axiom VI, 9 is $S^r_q(8)$, 10 is $S^q_p(9)$, 11 is $S^p_r(10)$, and 12 is 7, 11, mp.

Theorem 5. $p \vee p \rightarrow p$ is provable.

Proof: 1. $(p \rightarrow r) \rightarrow ((q \rightarrow r) \rightarrow (p \vee q \rightarrow r))$
2. $(p \rightarrow p) \rightarrow ((q \rightarrow p) \rightarrow (p \vee q \rightarrow p))$
3. $p \rightarrow p$
4. $(q \rightarrow p) \rightarrow (p \vee q \rightarrow p)$
5. $(p \rightarrow p) \rightarrow (p \vee p \rightarrow p)$
6. $p \vee p \rightarrow p$.

In this proof, 1 is axiom V, 2 is $S^p_r(1)$, 3 is Theorem 2, 4 is 2, 3, mp, 5 is $S^p_q(4)$, and 6 is 3, 5, mp.

Theorem 6. $p \rightarrow p \;\&\; p$ is provable.

Proof: 1. $(r \rightarrow p) \rightarrow ((r \rightarrow q) \rightarrow (r \rightarrow p \;\&\; q))$
2. $(p \rightarrow p) \rightarrow ((p \rightarrow q) \rightarrow (p \rightarrow p \;\&\; q))$
3. $p \rightarrow p$
4. $(p \rightarrow q) \rightarrow (p \rightarrow p \;\&\; q)$
5. $(p \rightarrow p) \rightarrow (p \rightarrow p \;\&\; p)$
6. $p \rightarrow p \;\&\; p$.

In this proof, 1 is axiom VIII, 2 is S^p_r (1), 3 is Theorem 2, 4 is 2, 3, mp, 5 is $S^p_q(4)$, and 6 is 3, 5, mp.

Theorem 7. $p \rightarrow p \vee p$ is provable.

Proof: 1. $p \rightarrow p \vee q$
2. $p \rightarrow p \vee p$.

In this proof, 1 is axiom III, and 2 is S^p_q (1).

Theorem 8. $p \;\&\; p \rightarrow p$ is provable.

Proof: 1. $p \;\&\; q \rightarrow p$
2. $p \;\&\; p \rightarrow p$.

In this proof, 1 is axiom VI, and 2 is $S^p_q(1)$.

Theorem 9. $\overline{\overline{\overline{p}}} \to \overline{p}$ is provable.

Proof: 1. $\overline{\overline{p}} \to p$

2. $\overline{\overline{\overline{p}}} \to \overline{p}$.

In this proof 1 is axiom XI, and 2 is $S^{p}_{\overline{p}}(1)$.

Theorem 10. $\overline{V} \to \overline{p}$ is provable.

Proof: 1. $(p \to q) \to (\overline{q} \to \overline{p})$

2. $(p \to V) \to (\overline{V} \to \overline{p})$

3. $p \to V$

4. $\overline{V} \to \overline{p}$.

In this proof, 1 is axiom IX, 2 is $S^{V}_{q}(1)$, 3 is Theorem 1, and 4 is 2, 3, mp.

Theorem 11. $\overline{p \vee q} \to \overline{p} \;\&\; \overline{q}$ is provable.

Proof: 1. $(p \to q) \to (\overline{q} \to \overline{p})$

2. $(p \to p \vee q) \to (\overline{p \vee q} \to \overline{p})$

3. $p \to p \vee q$

4. $\overline{p \vee q} \to \overline{p}$

5. $(r \to q) \to (\overline{q} \to \overline{r})$

6. $(r \to p \vee q) \to (\overline{p \vee q} \to \overline{r})$

7. $(q \to p \vee q) \to (\overline{p \vee q} \to \overline{q})$

8. $q \to p \vee q$

9. $\overline{p \vee q} \to \overline{q}$

10. $(r \to p) \to ((r \to q) \to (r \to p \;\&\; q))$

11. $(r \to \overline{p}) \to ((r \to q) \to (r \to \overline{p} \;\&\; q))$

12. $(r \to \overline{p}) \to ((r \to \overline{q}) \to (r \to \overline{p} \;\&\; \overline{q}))$

13. $(\overline{p \vee q} \rightarrow \bar{p}) \rightarrow ((\overline{p \vee q} \rightarrow \bar{q}) \rightarrow (\overline{p \vee q} \rightarrow \bar{p} \ \& \ \bar{q}))$
14. $(\overline{p \vee q} \rightarrow \bar{q}) \rightarrow (\overline{p \vee q} \rightarrow \bar{p} \ \& \ \bar{q})$
15. $\overline{p \vee q} \rightarrow \bar{p} \ \& \ \bar{q}$.

In this proof, 1 is axiom IX, 2 is $S_q^{p \vee q}(1)$, 3 is axiom III, 4 is 2, 3, mp, 5 is $S_p^r(1)$, 6 is $S_q^{p \vee q}(5)$, 7 is $S_r^q(6)$, 8 is axiom IV, 9 is 7, 8, mp, 10 is axiom VIII, 11 is $S_p^{\bar{p}}(10)$, 12 is $S_q^{\bar{q}}(11)$, 13 is $S_r^{\overline{p \vee q}}(12)$, 14 is 4, 13, mp, and 15 is 9, 14, mp.

We shall give the name *lemma* to any justifiable assertion that when certain formulae are provable, then a certain other formula is also provable. (Such justifiable assertions are often called *derived* rules in the literature.)

Lemma 1. If $A \rightarrow B$ and $B \rightarrow C$ are provable, then $A \rightarrow C$ is provable.

Proof: Suppose

1. $A \rightarrow B$
2. $B \rightarrow C$

are provable. Let D_1 designate a propositional variable that is not p and that has no occurrences in $B \rightarrow C$; let D_2 designate a propositional variable that is not p and that has no occurrences in A; and let D_3 designate a propositional variable that is not p or D_2 and that has no occurrences in A or in B. The reasons for these restrictions are explained at the end of the present chapter (pages 17–18).

3. $p \rightarrow (q \rightarrow p)$
4. $p \rightarrow (D_1 \rightarrow p)$
5. $(B \rightarrow C) \rightarrow (D_1 \rightarrow (B \rightarrow C))$
6. $(B \rightarrow C) \rightarrow (A \rightarrow (B \rightarrow C))$
7. $A \rightarrow (B \rightarrow C)$
8. $(p \rightarrow (q \rightarrow r)) \rightarrow ((p \rightarrow q) \rightarrow (p \rightarrow r))$
9. $(p \rightarrow (D_2 \rightarrow r)) \rightarrow ((p \rightarrow D_2) \rightarrow (p \rightarrow r))$
10. $(p \rightarrow (D_2 \rightarrow D_3)) \rightarrow ((p \rightarrow D_2) \rightarrow (p \rightarrow D_3))$

11. $(A \to (D_2 \to D_3)) \to ((A \to D_2) \to (A \to D_3))$
12. $(A \to (B \to D_3)) \to ((A \to B) \to (A \to D_3))$
13. $(A \to (B \to C)) \to ((A \to B) \to (A \to C))$
14. $(A \to B) \to (A \to C)$
15. $A \to C$.

In this proof, 3 is axiom I, 4 is $S_q^{D_1}(3)$, 5 is $S_p^{B \to C}(4)$, 6 is $S_{D_1}^A(5)$, 7 is 2, 6, mp, 8 is axiom II, 9 is $S_q^{D_2}(8)$, 10 is $S_r^{D_3}(9)$, 11 is $S_p^A(10)$, 12 is $S_{D_2}^B(11)$, 13 is $S_{D_3}^C(12)$, 14 is 7, 13, mp, and 15 is 1, 14, mp.

Lemma 1 is usually called the *syllogistic principle*. We shall refer to it as syll.

Lemma 2. If $A \to C$ is provable, then $A \ \& B \to C$ is provable.

Proof: Suppose

1. $A \to C$:

is provable. Let D_1 be a propositional variable different from q and having no occurrences in B.

2. $p \ \& \ q \to p$
3. $D_1 \ \& \ q \to D_1$
4. $D_1 \ \& \ B \to D_1$
5. $A \ \& \ B \to A$
6. $A \ \& \ B \to C$.

In this proof, 2 is axiom VI, 3 is $S_p^{D_1}(2)$, 4 is $S_q^B(3)$, 5 is $S_{D_1}^A(4)$, and 6 is 1, 5, syll.

Lemma 3. If $A \to (B \to C)$ is provable, then $A \ \& B \to C$ is provable.

Proof: Suppose

1. $A \to (B \to C)$

is provable. Let D_1 be a propositional variable that is different from p, q, and r and that has no occurrences in A or in B, and let D_2 be a propositional variable that is different from p and D_1 and that has no occurrences in A or in B.

2. $(p\to(q\to r))\to((p\to q)\to(p\to r))$
3. $(p\to(D_1\to r))\to((p\to D_1)\to(p\to r))$
4. $(p\to(D_1\to D_2))\to((p\to D_1)\to(p\to D_2))$
5. $(A \,\&\, B\to(D_1\to D_2))\to((A \,\&\, B\to D_1)$
   $\to(A \,\&\, B\to D_2))$
6. $(A \,\&\, B\to(B\to D_2))\to((A \,\&\, B\to B)$
   $\to(A \,\&\, B\to D_2))$
7. $(A \,\&\, B\to(B\to C))\to((A \,\&\, B\to B)$
   $\to(A \,\&\, B\to C))$
8. $A \,\&\, B\to(B\to C)$
9. $(A \,\&\, B\to B)\to(A \,\&\, B\to C)$
10. $p \,\&\, q\to q$
11. $D_1 \,\&\, q\to q$
12. $D_1 \,\&\, B\to B$
13. $A \,\&\, B\to B$
14. $A \,\&\, B\to C$.

In this proof, 2 is axiom II, 3 is $S_q^{D_1}(2)$, 4 is $S_r^{D_2}(3)$, 5 is $S_p^{A \,\&\, B}(4)$, 6 is $S_{D_1}^{B}(5)$, 7 is $S_{D_2}^{C}(6)$, 8 is obtained by applying Lemma 2 to step 1, 9 is 7, 8, mp, 10 is axiom VII, 11 is $S_p^{D_1}(10)$, 12 is $S_q^{B}(11)$, 13 is $S_{D_1}^{A}(12)$, and 14 is 9, 13, mp.

Lemma 3 is usually called the *unification of premisses principle*. We shall refer to it as unif.

Theorem 12. $\overline{V}\to p$ is provable.

Proof:

1. $V\to p$
2. $\overline{V}\to\bar{\bar{p}}$
3. $\bar{\bar{p}}\to p$
4. $\overline{V}\to p$.

In this proof, 1 is Theorem 10, 2 is $S^{\bar{p}}_{p}(1)$, 3 is axiom XI, 4 is 2, 3, syll.

Theorem 13. $p \,\&\, \bar{p} \rightarrow \bar{V}$ is provable.

Proof: 1. $p \rightarrow (q \rightarrow p)$
2. $p \rightarrow (V \rightarrow p)$
3. $(p \rightarrow q) \rightarrow (\bar{q} \rightarrow \bar{p})$
4. $(p \rightarrow r) \rightarrow (\bar{r} \rightarrow \bar{p})$
5. $(V \rightarrow r) \rightarrow (\bar{r} \rightarrow \bar{V})$
6. $(V \rightarrow p) \rightarrow (\bar{p} \rightarrow \bar{V})$
7. $p \rightarrow (\bar{p} \rightarrow \bar{V})$
8. $p \,\&\, \bar{p} \rightarrow \bar{V}$.

In this proof, 1 is axiom I, 2 is $S^{V}_{p}(1)$, 3 is axiom IX, 4 is $S^{r}_{q}(3)$, 5 is $S^{V}_{p}(4)$, 6 is $S^{p}_{r}(5)$, 7 is 2, 6, syll, and 8 is 7, unif.

Theorem 14. $p \vee \bar{p}$ is provable.

Proof: To simplify the proof, let V be any provable formula with no occurrences of p.

1. $\overline{p \vee q} \rightarrow \bar{p} \,\&\, \bar{q}$
2. $\overline{p \vee \bar{p}} \rightarrow \bar{p} \,\&\, \bar{\bar{p}}$
3. $p \,\&\, \bar{p} \rightarrow \bar{V}$
4. $\bar{p} \,\&\, \bar{\bar{p}} \rightarrow \bar{V}$
5. $\overline{p \vee \bar{p}} \rightarrow \bar{V}$
6. $(p \rightarrow q) \rightarrow (\bar{q} \rightarrow \bar{p})$
7. $(p \rightarrow \bar{V}) \rightarrow (\bar{\bar{V}} \rightarrow \bar{p})$
8. $(\overline{p \vee \bar{p}} \rightarrow \bar{V}) \rightarrow (\bar{\bar{V}} \rightarrow \overline{\overline{p \vee \bar{p}}})$

9. $\overline{\overline{V}} \to \overline{\overline{p \vee \overline{p}}}$

10. $p \to \overline{\overline{p}}$

11. $V \to \overline{\overline{V}}$

12. $V \to \overline{\overline{p \vee \overline{p}}}$

13. V

14. $\overline{\overline{p \vee \overline{p}}}$

15. $\overline{\overline{p}} \to p$

16. $\overline{\overline{p \vee \overline{p}}} \to p \vee \overline{p}$

17. $p \vee \overline{p}$.

In this proof, 1 is Theorem 11, 2 is $S^{\overline{p}}_{q}(1)$, 3 is Theorem 13, 4 is $S^{\overline{p}}_{p}(3)$, 5 is 2, 4, syll, 6 is axiom IX, 7 is $S^{V}_{q}(6)$, 8 is $S^{\overline{p \vee \overline{p}}}_{p}(7)$, 9 is 5, 8, mp, 10 is axiom X, 11 is $S^{V}_{p}(10)$, 12 is 9, 11, syll, 13 is provable (by notational definition), 14 is 12, 13, mp, 15 is axiom XI, 16 is $S^{p \vee \overline{p}}_{p}(15)$, and 17 is 14, 16, mp.

The reasons for the restrictions imposed on D_1, D_2, and D_3 in the proofs of Lemmas 1, 2, and 3 may be explained as follows.

(i) It was pointed out at the end of Ch. 2 that the order in which substitutions are made may materially affect the final outcome. The question of order arises because our rule of substitution is a weak one. It permits only one propositional variable to be substituted for at any one step and does not, therefore, permit simultaneous substitutions of several propositional variables. Considering an example, if we wish to obtain

(1) $p \vee q \to (r \mathbin{\&} p \to p \vee q)$

as a step in a proof, then we start from

(2) $p \to (q \to p)$,

which is axiom I, and then use the rule of substitution. If we substitute first for p in (2) we get

(3) $p \vee q \to (q \to p \vee q)$.

We cannot now deduce (1) from (3) by substituting r & p for q in (3), for $S_q^{r \,\&\, p}(\,(3)\,)$ is

(4) $p \vee r \,\&\, p \to (r \,\&\, p \to p \vee r \,\&\, p)$,

which is not (1). The trouble arises because the first substituting formula, $p \vee q$, contains the propositional variable q which the second substituting formula, r & p, is to replace. Our way of overcoming this difficulty is to proceed to (1) by substituting say r for q in (2), getting

(5) $p \to (r \to p)$,

then substituting $p \vee q$ for p, getting

(6) $p \vee q \to (r \to p \vee q)$,

finally substituting r & p for r in (6) to obtain (1). Cf. the use of r in steps 4 and 9 of the proofs of Theorems 3 and 4. The *final* effect is always *as if* simultaneous substitutions were allowed.

(ii) Considering another example, let us go back to the proof of Lemma 1. If, in step 5, the propositional variable designated by D_1 were to occur in B or C and so in $B \to C$, then on substituting A for D_1 to get step 6 either B or C would be altered by each occurrence of D_1 in it becoming an occurrence of A, with the result that $B \to C$ would not remain intact. Hence, D_1 must have no occurrences in $B \to C$ and the easiest way to ensure this is to choose D_1 to be a propositional variable that has no occurrences in B or in C; such a choice is always possible for there are infinitely many variables available, by Ch. 1 (i).

Chapter Five

HYPOTHETICAL DEDUCTION

Suppose that, in addition to the axioms of P, we allow *ad hoc* hypotheses as premisses from which to make deductions. For example, we may consider problems of the kind: (i) if $p \to (q \to r)$ is adopted as a hypothesis, would it yield $(p \to q) \to (p \to r)$, and would it yield $p \,\&\, q \to r$? (ii) if A and B are adopted as hypotheses, would they yield $A \,\&\, B$? These questions can be expressed by using the sign $\vdash$, called the *turnstile*, which is read as 'yields' or 'yield', according as there is one or more than one hypothesis. (i) becomes: is it true that $p \to (q \to r) \vdash (p \to q) \to (p \to r)$, and that $p \to (q \to r) \vdash p \,\&\, q \to r$? (ii) becomes: is it true that $A, B \vdash A \,\&\, B$? The exact sense of $\vdash$ is determined by the following definition. (Some other books employ a rather different definition.)

Definition 4. (*a*) $A_1, A_2, \ldots, A_n \vdash A_j$ ($j=1, 2, \ldots, n$). (*b*) If B is provable, then $A_1, A_2, \ldots, A_n \vdash B$. (*c*) If $A_1, A_2, \ldots, A_n \vdash B$ and $A_1, A_2, \ldots, A_n \vdash B \to C$, then $A_1, A_2, \ldots, A_n \vdash C$. (*d*) $A_1, A_2, \ldots, A_n$ yield no other formulae than those specified to be yielded by them by (*a*), (*b*), or (*c*).

It is very convenient to allow $\vdash$ to be used when there are no hypotheses; this is the case when $n=0$. $\vdash B$ then signifies that B is provable.

It is to be noticed carefully that although Definition 4 has a clause—(*c*)—relating to the rule of *modus ponens*, it has not a corresponding clause relating to the rule of substitution. In fact, if certain hypotheses yield B, it is not true, in general, that, D being a propositional variable, they also yield $S_D^C(B)$.

Let us consider some examples.

Example 1. Is it true that

(1) $p\to(q\to r), p \ \& \ q \vdash r$?

The working may be set out as follows.

1. $p\to(q\to r)^\circ$
2. $p \ \& \ q^\circ$
3. $p \ \& \ q\to p$
4. p
5. $q\to r$
6. $p \ \& \ q\to q$
7. q
8. r.

Steps 1 and 2 here are marked by small superscript circles to indicate that they are hypotheses. 3 is axiom VI. 4 is 2, 3, mp. 4 is yielded by the hypotheses because 2 and 3 are themselves yielded by the hypotheses, by Definition 4 (*a*), (*b*). 5 is 1, 4, mp. Again, 5 is yielded by the hypotheses, by Definition 4 (*c*), because 1 and 4 are yielded by the hypotheses. 6 is axiom VII. 7 is 2, 6, mp. 7 is yielded by the hypotheses, by Definition (*c*), because 2 and 6 are yielded by the hypotheses, by Definition 4 (*a*), (*b*). Finally, 8 is 5, 7, mp, and, being obtained by *modus ponens* from steps that are themselves yielded by the hypotheses, is itself yielded by the hypotheses. Hence, (1) is true.

Example 2. Is it true that

(2) $p\to(q\to r)\vdash p \ \& \ q\to r$?

If our working is

1. $p\to(q\to r)^\circ$
2. $(p\to(q\to r))\to((p\to q)\to(p\to r))$
3. $(p\to q)\to(p\to r)$

4. $(p \ \& \ q \to q) \to (p \ \& \ q \to r)$
5. $p \ \& \ q \to q$
6. $p \ \& \ q \to r$,

then we should not have shown that (2) is true. While each of steps 1, 2, and 3 is yielded by the hypothesis, (i) it has not been shown that 3 is provable (although it has been shown that 1 yields 3), (ii) 4 has been obtained from 3 by substitution, and (iii) there is no clause in Definition 4 which permits us to say that $S_p^{p \,\&\, q}(3)$ is yielded by the hypothesis. (Why there is no such clause will be clarified later; cf. pages 38–40.)

Nevertheless, (2) is true, as may be shown by constructing a proof along the lines of the proof of Ch. 4, Lemma 3.

Example 3. Is it true that

(3) $p \vdash q \to r$?

If our working is

1. p°
2. $p \to (q \to p)$
3. $q \to p$
4. $q \to r$,

then we should not have shown that (3) is true. While each of steps 1, 2, and 3 is yielded by the hypothesis, it has not been shown that 3 is provable, and 4 has been obtained from 3 by substitution. In any case, (3) is not true.

Example 4. Is it true that

(4) $q \vdash r \to q$?

If our working is

1. q°
2. $p \to (q \to p)$
3. $p \to (r \to p)$
4. $q \to (r \to q)$
5. $r \to q$,

then we should have shown that (4) is true. 1 is a hypothesis and 1 yields 1. 2 is axiom I and 1 yields 2.

3 is $S^r_q(2)$, and since 2 is provable, 3 is provable; so, by Definition 4 (*b*), 1 yields 3. 4 is $S^q_p(3)$, and since 3 is provable, 4 is also provable, so, again, 1 yields 4. Finally, 5 is 1, 4, mp, and being got from two steps that are yielded by 1, 5 is itself yielded by 1, by virtue of Definition 4 (*c*).

Thus, in dealing with hypotheses, the use of the rule of substitution is legitimate if it is applied to a formula that has been shown to be provable or that is provable; on the other hand, its use ruins what is intended as a proof if it is applied to a formula that has not been shown to be provable or that is not provable.

Chapter Six

COURSE-OF-VALUES INDUCTION

In proving theorems about P it is frequently necessary or advantageous to employ an arithmetical method. This method is called *course-of-values induction*. The method is applied in proving theorems which involve either the non-negative whole numbers 0, 1, 2, 3, . . . or the positive whole numbers 1, 2, 3, . . . Theorems about P can involve whole numbers in a variety of ways. One way is in the number of occurrences of propositional variables that a formula of P contains. Another way is in the number of occurrences of connectives that a formula of P contains. A third way is in the number of hypotheses employed to yield a certain formula. A fourth way is in the number of steps in the proof of a certain formula. A fifth way is in the number of steps in a hypothetical deduction of a certain formula from such-and-such hypotheses.

Let T be a theorem which involves numbers. We shall write $T(0)$, $T(1)$, $T(2)$, . . . , $T(n)$ to signify those cases of T when 0, 1, 2, . . . , n respectively are involved. By the notation $T(k \leq m)$ we shall signify those cases of T when any number k not greater than m is involved.

The method of course-of-values induction may be expressed in the form of a rule of reasoning:

If it has been proved that $T(0)$ is true and it has been

proved that $T(k \leq m)$ implies $T(m+1)$ for any m, then it is permissible to conclude that $T(m)$ is true for each m.

In this formulation k and m range over the non-negative numbers. Another form of the rule has $T(1)$ in the place of $T(0)$, and in this second formulation k and m range over the positive numbers.

To justify the method of course-of-values induction we assume the truth of the premisses, $T(0)$, and $T(k \leq m)$ implies $T(m+1)$ for any m, and attempt to show the truth of the conclusion that $T(m)$ for each m. Now, if $T(k \leq m)$ implies $T(m+1)$ for any m, then $T(k \leq 0)$ implies $T(0+1)$. Since $T(k \leq 0)$ is $T(0)$, $T(0)$ implies $T(1)$. *Ex hypothesi*, $T(0)$ is true. Therefore, $T(1)$ is true, for whatever is implied by a true statement is itself true. Next, $T(k \leq 1)$ implies $T(1+1)$. But $T(k \leq 1)$ is true since $T(0)$ and $T(1)$ are true. Therefore, $T(2)$ is true. Proceeding similarly, one can show that each of $T(3)$, $T(4)$, ... is true, that is one can show the truth of $T(m)$ for each m.

The justification of the form of the method of course-of-values induction when $T(1)$ instead of $T(0)$ is used as a premiss is essentially the same as the justification just given.

The value and the functioning of course-of-values induction will be better understood and appreciated when Ch. 7 has been studied.

Chapter Seven

THE DEDUCTION THEOREM

In this chapter we prove a basic theorem about P. This theorem is called the *deduction theorem*. According to this theorem, if $A \vdash B$, then $\vdash A \rightarrow B$; if $A, C \vdash B$, then $A \vdash C \rightarrow B$, and so, by the preceding case, $\vdash A \rightarrow (C \rightarrow B)$; if $A, C, D \vdash B$, then $A, C \vdash D \rightarrow B$, and so, by the preceding cases, $A \vdash C \rightarrow (D \rightarrow B)$ and $\vdash A \rightarrow (C \rightarrow (D \rightarrow B))$; and similarly for any number of hypotheses. What the theorem tells us is that, for example, if

(1) $p \rightarrow (q \rightarrow r), p \ \& \ q \vdash r$,

then

(2) $\vdash (p \rightarrow (q \rightarrow r)) \rightarrow (p \ \& \ q \rightarrow r)$;

therefore if we know that (1) is true (which it is, cf. Ch. 5, Example 1), we shall know also that (2) is true, that is, we shall know that the formula following the turnstile is provable. The help afforded by the deduction theorem arises from the fact that, for example, (1) is very much easier to prove directly than (2) is; hypothetical deductions are, in general, incomparably more readily performed than deductions that make no use of hypotheses as premisses.

If $A_1, A_2, \ldots, A_n \vdash B$, then there is a hypothetical deduction of B from the hypotheses A_i, this deduction containing B as the step numbered k ($k=1$ or 2 or $\ldots$); e.g., the hypothetical deduction in Ch. 5, Example 1 of r from $p \rightarrow (q \rightarrow r)$ and $p \ \& \ q$ contains r as the step numbered 8. For any formula B that is yielded by n

hypotheses A_i there is some hypothetical deduction of B from those hypotheses such that B is contained in the deduction as the step numbered k. To indicate that B is contained as the step numbered k we write A_1, $A_2, \ldots, A_n \vdash_k B$.

The Deduction Theorem. If $A_1, A_2, \ldots, A_n \vdash B$, then $A_1, A_2, \ldots, A_{n-1} \vdash A_n \rightarrow B$.

Proof. We proceed by course-of-values induction, starting, in the notation of Ch. 6, with $T(1)$.

$T(1)$: If $A_1, A_2, \ldots, A_n \vdash_1 B$, then $A_1, A_2, \ldots, A_{n-1} \vdash A_n \rightarrow B$.

Before proving that $T(1)$ is true, attention should be drawn to the absence of any number being affixed to the turnstile in the consequent of $T(1)$; this means that no limitation is placed on the number of steps there may be in the hypothetical deduction of $A_n \rightarrow B$ from the hypotheses A_1 to A_{n-1}.

The standard way of establishing the truth of a conditional statement, such as $T(1)$, is to suppose the truth of the antecedent and to derive the consequent as a conclusion from that supposed truth. Therefore we begin by supposing that $A_1, A_2, \ldots, A_n \vdash_1 B$. Then either (*a*) B is some A_j ($j=1$ or 2 or $\ldots$ or $n-1$), or (*b*) B is A_n, or (*c*) B is provable. (These three alternatives are not necessarily mutually exclusive.)

(*a*) If B is A_j ($j=1$ or 2 or $\ldots$ or $n-1$), then a hypothetical deduction of $A_n \rightarrow B$ from A_1 to A_{n-1} may be constructed as follows, where D is a propositional variable that is different from p and has no occurrences in A_j;

1\. 1——1. $n-1$. $A_1, A_2, \ldots, A_{n-1}$°
2\. $p \rightarrow (q \rightarrow p)$
3\. $p \rightarrow (D \rightarrow p)$

4. $A_j \to (D \to A_j)$
5. $A_j \to (A_n \to A_j)$
6. $A_n \to A_j$.

In this deduction, 1 is divided into $n-1$ sub-steps, one for each hypothesis A_i, 2 is axiom 1, 3 is $S_q^D(2)$, 4 is $S_p^{A_j}(3)$, 5 is $S_D^{A_n}(4)$, and 6 is $1.j$, 5, mp.

(*b*) If B is A_n, then a hypothetical deduction of $A_n \to B$ (i.e., of $A_n \to A_n$) from A_1 to A_{n-1} may be constructed as follows:

1. 1——1. $n-1$. $A_1, A_2, \ldots, A_{n-1}$°
2. $p \to p$
3. $A_n \to A_n$.

In this deduction, 2 is Ch. 4, Theorem 2, and 3 is $S_p^{A_n}(2)$.

(*c*) If B is provable, then a hypothetical deduction of $A_n \to B$ from A_1 to A_{n-1} may be constructed as follows, where D is a propositional variable that is different from p and has no occurrences in B:

1. 1——1. $n-1$. $A_1, A_2, \ldots, A_{n-1}$°
2. B
3. $p \to (q \to p)$
4. $p \to (D \to p)$
5. $B \to (D \to B)$
6. $B \to (A_n \to B)$
7. $A_n \to B$.

In this deduction, 3 is axiom I, 4 is $S_q(3)$, 5 is $S_p^B(4)$, 6 is $S_D^{A_n}(5)$, and 7 is 2, 6, mp.

Thus, it has been shown that $T(1)$ is true.

Next, we wish to establish that if $T(k \leq m)$ is true, then $T(m+1)$ is true, k and m being any positive whole numbers. Therefore, we suppose

$T(k \leq m)$: If $A_1, A_2, \ldots, A_n \vdash_{k \leq m} B$, then $A_1, A_2, \ldots$ $A_{n-1} \vdash A_n \to B$,

and attempt to derive as conclusion the truth of

$T(m+1)$: If $A_1, A_2, \ldots, A_n \vdash_{m+1} B$, then $A_1, A_2, \ldots, A_{n-1} \vdash A_n \rightarrow B$.

If B is yielded by A_1 to A_n in $m+1$ steps, then either (*a*) B is some A_j ($j=1$ or 2 or ... or $n-1$), or (*b*) B is A_n, or (*c*) B is provable, or (*d*) B is deduced by *modus ponens* from two preceding steps C and $C \rightarrow B$ that are themselves yielded by A_1 to A_n. Cases (*a*), (*b*), and (*c*) are dealt with in exactly the same way as (*a*), (*b*), and (*c*) above. It remains to deal with (*d*).

(*d*) If B is deduced by *modus ponens* from two preceding steps C and $C \rightarrow B$, then, since B occurs as the step numbered $m+1$, these steps must bear some number k where $k \leq m$. By the supposed truth of $T(k \leq m)$, $A_n \rightarrow C$ and $A_n \rightarrow (C \rightarrow B)$ are yielded by the hypotheses A_1 to A_{n-1}. A hypothetical deduction of $A_n \rightarrow B$ from A_1 to A_{n-1} may be constructed as follows, where D is a propositional variable that is not p or r and has no occurrences in A_n, and D_1 is a propositional variable that is not p or D and has no occurrences in A_n or C:

1. 1——1. $n-1$. $A_1, A_2, \ldots, A_{n-1}$°
2. $A_n \rightarrow C$
3. $A_n \rightarrow (C \rightarrow B)$
4. $(p \rightarrow (q \rightarrow r)) \rightarrow ((p \rightarrow q) \rightarrow (p \rightarrow r))$
5. $(p \rightarrow (D \rightarrow r)) \rightarrow ((p \rightarrow D) \rightarrow (p \rightarrow r))$
6. $(p \rightarrow (D \rightarrow D_1)) \rightarrow ((p \rightarrow D) \rightarrow (p \rightarrow D_1))$
7. $(A_n \rightarrow (D \rightarrow D_1)) \rightarrow ((A_n \rightarrow D) \rightarrow (A_n \rightarrow D_1))$
8. $(A_n \rightarrow (C \rightarrow D_1)) \rightarrow ((A_n \rightarrow C) \rightarrow (A_n \rightarrow D_1))$
9. $(A_n \rightarrow (C \rightarrow B)) \rightarrow ((A_n \rightarrow C) \rightarrow (A_n \rightarrow B))$
10. $(A_n \rightarrow C) \rightarrow (A_n \rightarrow B)$
11. $A_n \rightarrow B$.

In this deduction, 2 and 3 are given, by the supposition of $T(k \leq m)$, to be yielded by the initial hypotheses, 4 is axiom II, 5 is $S^D_q(4)$, 6 is $S^{D_1}_r(5)$, 7 is $S^{A_n}_p(6)$, 8 is

$S_D^C(7)$, 9 is $S_{D_1}^B(8)$, 10 is 3, 9, mp, and 11 is 2, 10, mp.

We have shown that $T(1)$ is true and that $T(k \leq m)$ implies $T(m+1)$ for any $m \geq 1$. We are therefore entitled to conclude that $T(m)$ is true for each $m \geq 1$, that is, to conclude that no matter how many steps it takes for A_1 to A_n to yield B, it is true that $A_n \rightarrow B$ is yielded by A_1 to A_{n-1}.

Chapter Eight

SOME APPLICATIONS OF THE DEDUCTION THEOREM

Suppose one wishes to show that a formula (i) $A \to B$ [i.e., a formula of the form $A \to B$] is provable. If one can show that (ii) $A \vdash B$, then it will follow, by one application of the deduction theorem to (ii), that (i) is provable; for the deduction theorem, when $n=1$, says: if $A \vdash B$, then $\vdash A \to B$. Again, suppose one wishes to show that a formula $A \to (B \to C)$ is provable. If one can show that $A, B \vdash C$, then it will follow, by two successive applications of the deduction theorem, that $A \to (B \to C)$ is provable; for by one application of the deduction theorem to $A, B \vdash C$ one obtains $A \vdash B \to C$, and by an application of the deduction theorem to this result one obtains $\vdash A \to (B \to C)$, i.e., $A \to (B \to C)$ is provable. One may proceed similarly when one wishes to show that formulae of the form $A \to (B \to (C \to D))$, $A \to (B \to (C \to (D \to E)))$, and so on, are provable.

Theorem 15. $p \to (q \to p \,\&\, q)$ is provable.

Proof: 1. p°
2. q°
3. $(r \to p) \to ((r \to q) \to (r \to p \,\&\, q))$
4. $(q \to p) \to ((q \to q) \to (q \to p \,\&\, q))$
5. $p \to (q \to p)$
6. $q \to p$

7. $(q \to q) \to (q \to p \,\&\, q)$
8. $p \to p$
9. $q \to q$
10. $q \to p \,\&\, q$
11. $p \,\&\, q$.

In this deduction, 3 is axiom VIII, 4 is $S^q_r(3)$, 5 is axiom I, 6 is 1, 5, mp, 7 is 4, 6, mp, 8 is Ch. 4, Theorem 2, 9 is $S^q_p(8)$, 10 is 7, 9, mp, and 11 is 2, 10, mp. What this deduction establishes is that $p, q \vdash p \,\&\, q$. By applying the deduction theorem one obtains $p \vdash q \to p \,\&\, q$. By applying the deduction theorem to this result one obtains $\vdash p \to (q \to p \,\&\, q)$.

Theorem 16. $(p \to q) \to ((p \to (q \to r)) \to (p \to r))$ is provable.

Proof: 1. $p \to q^{\circ}$
2. $p \to (q \to r)^{\circ}$
3. p°
4. $q \to r$
5. q
6. r.

In this deduction, 4 is 2, 3, mp, 5 is 1, 3, mp, and 6 is 4, 5, mp. What this deduction shows is that

(1) $p \to q, p \to (q \to r), p \vdash r$.

By applying the deduction theorem to (1) one obtains

(2) $p \to q, p \to (q \to r) \vdash p \to r$.

By applying the deduction theorem to (2) one obtains

(3) $p \to q \vdash (p \to (q \to r)) \to (p \to r)$.

Finally, by applying the deduction theorem to (3) one obtains

(4) $\vdash (p \to q) \to ((p \to (q \to r)) \to (p \to r))$.

(4) may be described briefly as being obtainable from three successive applications of the deduction theorem to (1).

Theorem 17. $(p \to q) \to ((q \to r) \to (p \to r))$ is provable.

Proof: 1. $p \to q^{\circ}$
2. $q \to r^{\circ}$
3. p°
4. q
5. r.

In this deduction, 4 is 1, 3, mp, and 5 is 2, 4, mp. What this deduction shows is that

(5) $p \to q,\ q \to r,\ p \vdash r$.

The theorem is obtainable from three successive applications of the deduction theorem to (5):

(6) $\vdash (p \to q) \to ((q \to r) \to (p \to r))$.

From Theorem 17 it follows, by using the rule of substitution, that

(7) $(A \to B) \to ((B \to C) \to (A \to C))$ is provable.

Compare Ch. 4, Lemma 1 and the proof thereof.

Theorem 18. $(p \to q) \to (p \,\&\, r \to q)$ is provable.

Proof: 1. $p \to q^{\circ}$
2. $p \,\&\, r^{\circ}$
3. $p \,\&\, q \to p$
4. $p \,\&\, r \to p$
5. p
6. q.

In this deduction, 3 is axiom VI, 4 is $S^{r}_{q}(3)$, 5 is 2, 4, mp, and 6 is 1, 5, mp. What this deduction shows is that

(8) $p \to q,\ p \,\&\, r \vdash q$.

The theorem is obtainable from two successive applications of the deduction theorem to (8).

From Theorem 18 it follows, by using the rule of substitution, that

(9) $(A \to B) \to (A \,\&\, C \to B)$ is provable.

Compare Ch. 4, Lemma 2 and the proof thereof.

Some Applications of the Deduction Theorem

Of course, the assertions that the symbolic expressions in (7) and (9) are provable are elliptical, the proper meaning being that each formula in P that is of the form of those symbolic expressions is a provable formula in P.

Theorem 19. $(p \to q) \to ((r \to p) \to (r \to q))$ is provable.

Proof: 1. $p \to q^{\circ}$
2. $r \to p^{\circ}$
3. r°
4. p
5. q.

In this deduction, 4 is 2, 3, mp, and 5 is 1, 4, mp. What this deduction shows is that

(10) $p \to q, r \to p, r \vdash q$.

The theorem is obtainable from three successive applications of the deduction theorem to (10).

Theorem 20. $(p \to (q \to r)) \to (q \to (p \to r))$ is provable.

Proof: 1. $p \to (q \to r)^{\circ}$
2. q°
3. p°
4. $q \to r$
5. r.

In this deduction, 4 is 1, 3, mp, and 5 is 2, 4, mp. What this deduction shows is that

(11) $p \to (q \to r), q, p \vdash r$.

The theorem is obtainable from three successive applications of the deduction theorem to (11).

Theorem 21. $(p \to (p \to q)) \to (p \to q)$ is provable.

Proof: 1. $p \to (p \to q)^{\circ}$
2. p°
3. $p \to q$
4. q.

In this deduction, 3 is 1, 2, mp, and 4 is 2, 3, mp. What this deduction shows is that

(12) $p \rightarrow (p \rightarrow q), p \vdash q$.

The theorem is obtainable from two successive applications of the deduction theorem to (12).

Theorem 22. $(p \rightarrow q) \rightarrow ((r \rightarrow (s \rightarrow p)) \rightarrow (r \rightarrow (s \rightarrow q)))$ is provable.

Proof: 1. $p \rightarrow q^{\circ}$
2. $r \rightarrow (s \rightarrow p)^{\circ}$
3. r°
4. s°
5. $s \rightarrow p$
6. p
7. q.

In this deduction, 5 is 2, 3, mp, 6 is 4, 5, mp, and 7 is 1, 6, mp. What this deduction shows is that

(13) $p \rightarrow q, r \rightarrow (s \rightarrow p), r, s \vdash q$.

The theorem is obtainable from four successive applications of the deduction theorem to (13).

Theorem 23. $((p \rightarrow q) \rightarrow (p \rightarrow r)) \rightarrow (p \rightarrow (q \rightarrow r))$ is provable.

Proof: 1. $(p \rightarrow q) \rightarrow (p \rightarrow r)^{\circ}$
2. p°
3. q°
4. $p \rightarrow (q \rightarrow p)$
5. $p \rightarrow (r \rightarrow p)$
6. $q \rightarrow (r \rightarrow q)$
7. $q \rightarrow (p \rightarrow q)$
8. $p \rightarrow q$
9. $p \rightarrow r$
10. r.

In this deduction, 4 is axiom I, 5 is $S_q^r(4)$, 6 is $S_p^q(5)$,

7 is $S^{p}_{r}(6)$, 8 is 3, 7, mp, 9 is 1, 8, mp, and 10 is 2, 9, mp. What this deduction shows is that

(14) $(p \to q) \to (p \to r), p, q \vdash r$.

The theorem is obtainable from three successive application of the deduction theorem to (14).

Theorem 24. $(p \to \bar{q}) \to (q \to \bar{p})$ is provable.

Proof:
1. $p \to \bar{q}^{\circ}$
2. q°
3. $(p \to q) \to (\bar{q} \to \bar{p})$
4. $(p \to \bar{q}) \to (\bar{\bar{q}} \to \bar{p})$
5. $\bar{\bar{q}} \to \bar{p}$
6. $p \to \bar{\bar{p}}$
7. $q \to \bar{\bar{q}}$
8. $\bar{\bar{q}}$
9. $\bar{p}$.

In this deduction, 3 is axiom IX, 4 is $S^{\bar{q}}_{q}(3)$, 5 is 1, 4, mp, 6 is axiom X, 7 is $S^{q}_{p}(6)$, 8 is 2, 7, mp, and 9 is 5, 8, mp. What this deduction shows is that

(15) $p \to \bar{q}, q \vdash \bar{p}$.

The theorem is obtainable from two successive applications of the deduction theorem to (15).

Henceforth, proofs will not always be given in full, some intermediate steps being omitted. A step that depends directly on omitted steps will be indicated by the number accompanying the occurring step in the proof having an asterisk affixed to it. A clue to how such a step is obtained will be given in the piece of text immediately following the proof.

Theorem 25. $(p \to q) \to ((p \to \bar{q}) \to \bar{p})$ is provable.

Proof: 1. $p \to q^{\circ}$

2. $p \to \bar{q}^{\circ}$

3. $(r \to p) \to ((r \to q) \to (r \to p \; \& \; q))$

*4. $(p \to q) \to ((p \to \bar{q}) \to (p \to q \; \& \; \bar{q}))$

5. $(p \to \bar{q}) \to (p \to q \; \& \; \bar{q})$

6. $p \to q \; \& \; \bar{q}$

7. $p \; \& \; \bar{p} \to \bar{V}$

8. $q \; \& \; \bar{q} \to \bar{V}$

9. $(p \to q) \to ((q \to r) \to (p \to r))$

*10. $(p \to q \; \& \; \bar{q}) \to ((q \; \& \; \bar{q} \to \bar{V}) \to (p \to \bar{V}))$

*11. $p \to \bar{V}$

*12. $(p \to \bar{V}) \to (\bar{\bar{V}} \to \bar{p})$

13. $\bar{\bar{V}} \to \bar{p}$

*14. $V \to \bar{\bar{V}}$

15. V

16. $\bar{\bar{V}}$

17. $\bar{p}$.

In this deduction, 3 is axiom VIII, 4 comes from 3 by substitution, 5 is 1, 4, mp, 6 is 2, 5, mp, 7 is Ch. 4, Theorem 13, 8 is $S^q_p(7)$, 9 is Theorem 17, 10 comes from 9 by substitution, 11 comes from 6, 8, and 10 by *modus ponens*, 12 comes from axiom IX by substitution, 13 is 11, 12, mp, 14 comes from axiom X by substitution, 15 is provable (by notational definition), 16 is 14, 15, mp, and 17 is 13, 16, mp. What this deduction shows is that

(16) $p \to q, \; p \to \bar{q} \vdash \bar{p}$.

The theorem is obtainable from two successive applications of the deduction theorem to (16).

Lemma 4. If $A_1, A_2, \ldots, A_n \vdash B$ and $A_1, A_2, \ldots, A_n \vdash \bar{B}$, then $A_1, A_2, \ldots, A_{n-1} \vdash \bar{A}_n$.

Proof: Applying the deduction theorem once to each clause in the antecedent of the Lemma, one obtains $A_1, A_2, \ldots, A_{n-1} \vdash A_n \rightarrow B$ and $A_1, A_2, \ldots, A_{n-1} \vdash A_n \rightarrow \bar{B}$. Hence,

1. 1——1. $n-1$. $A_1, A_2, \ldots, A_{n-1}{}^{\circ}$
2. $A_n \rightarrow B$
3. $A_n \rightarrow \bar{B}$
4. $(p \rightarrow q) \rightarrow ((p \rightarrow \bar{q}) \rightarrow \bar{p})$

*5. $(A_n \rightarrow B) \rightarrow ((A_n \rightarrow \bar{B}) \rightarrow \bar{A}_n)$

6. $\bar{A}_n$,

where 2 and 3 have been already shown to be yielded by the initial hypotheses, 4 is Theorem 25, 5 comes from 4 by substitution, and 6 comes from 2, 3, and 5 by *modus ponens.*

Theorem 26. $\overline{p \,\&\, \bar{p}}$ is provable.

Proof: (i) $p \,\&\, \bar{p} \vdash p$, for

1. $p \,\&\, \bar{p}^{\circ}$
2. $p \,\&\, q \rightarrow p$
3. $p \,\&\, \bar{p} \rightarrow p$
4. p,

where 2 is axiom VI, 3 is $S^{\bar{p}}_{q}(2)$, and 4 is 1, 3, mp.

(ii) $p \,\&\, \bar{p} \vdash \bar{p}$, for

1. $p \,\&\, \bar{p}^{\circ}$
2. $p \,\&\, q \rightarrow q$

$3.\ p\ \&\ \bar{p} \to \bar{p}$

$4.\ \bar{p},$

where 2 is axiom VII, 3 is $S^{\bar{p}}_{q}(2)$, and 4 is 1, 3, mp.

Applying Lemma 4 to (i) and (ii) gives $\vdash p\ \&\ \bar{p}$.

Theorem 27. $(p \to \bar{p}) \to \bar{p}$ is provable.

Proof: $1.\ p \to \bar{p}^{\circ}$

$2.\ (p \to q) \to ((p \to \bar{q}) \to \bar{p})$

$3.\ (p \to p) \to ((p \to \bar{p}) \to \bar{p})$

$4.\ p \to p$

$5.\ (p \to \bar{p}) \to \bar{p}$

$6.\ \bar{p}.$

In this deduction, 2 is Theorem 25, 3 is $S^{p}_{q}(2)$, 4 is Ch. 4, Theorem 2, 5 is 3, 4, mp, and 6 is 1, 5, mp. What this deduction shows is that

(17) $p \to \bar{p} \vdash \bar{p}$.

The theorem is obtainable from one application of the deduction theorem to (17).

It was pointed out in Ch. 5 that the rule of substitution cannot be used in establishing that a formula B is yielded by the hypotheses A_i unless the rule is applied to a provable formula (so that B itself is a provable formula). The reasons for imposing this restriction in the definition of $\vdash$ can be elucidated by an example. Suppose the restriction were not made, so that the hypotheses A_i yield B if B is deduced from a formula C that is yielded by the A_i, the deduction of B from C taking place by virtue of the rule of substitution. Then we should be able to show that $p \vdash r$, for

$1.\ p^{\circ}$

$2.\ p \to (q \to p)$

3. $q \rightarrow p$
4. $q \rightarrow r$
5. $p \rightarrow r$
6. r,

where 2 is axiom I, 3 is 1, 2, mp, 4 is $S^{r}_{p}(3)$, 5 is $S^{p}_{q}(4)$, and 6 is 1, 5, mp. By applying the deduction theorem to $p \vdash r$ we obtain that $p \rightarrow r$ is provable. Hence, $V \rightarrow p \,\&\, \bar{p}$ is provable, by the rule of substitution. Therefore, $p \,\&\, \bar{p}$ is provable, by the definition of V and *modus ponens*. There are two connected objections to this result. One is that we do not wish to have $p \,\&\, \bar{p}$ as a provable formula in P since it does not represent a valid logical principle and we wish all the provable formulae of P to represent only valid logical principles —otherwise there would be no discrimination in P between the valid and the invalid principles of logic. Secondly, it has been proved above (Theorem 26) that $\overline{p \,\&\, \bar{p}}$ is provable. So if $p \,\&\, \bar{p}$ is also provable, P would contain two provable formulae which contradict one another. From this contradiction it would follow that every formula A is provable in P, for

1. $p \,\&\, \bar{p}$
2. $\overline{p \,\&\, \bar{p}}$
3. $p \rightarrow (q \rightarrow p \,\&\, q)$

*4. $(p \,\&\, \bar{p}) \rightarrow (\overline{p \,\&\, \bar{p}} \rightarrow (p \,\&\, \bar{p}) \,\&\, \overline{p \,\&\, \bar{p}})$

*5. $(p \,\&\, \bar{p}) \,\&\, \overline{p \,\&\, \bar{p}}$

6. $p \,\&\, \bar{p} \rightarrow \bar{V}$
7. $(p \,\&\, \bar{p}) \,\&\, \overline{p \,\&\, \bar{p}} \rightarrow \bar{V}$
8. $\bar{V}$
9. $\bar{V} \rightarrow p$

10. p
11. A.

Here, 3 is Theorem 15, 4 comes from 3 by substitution, 5 comes from 1, 2, and 4 by *modus ponens*, 6 is Ch. 4, Theorem 13, 7 is $S_p^{p \,\&\, \bar{p}}(6)$, 8 is 5, 7, mp, 9 is Ch. 4, Theorem 12, 10 is 8, 9, mp, and 11 is $S_p^A(10)$.

Chapter Nine

NEGATIONS OF DISJUNCTIONS AND CONJUNCTIONS

The purpose of the present section is to show that

(1) $(\overline{p \vee q} \rightarrow \bar{p} \ \& \ \bar{q}) \ \& \ (\bar{p} \ \& \ \bar{q} \rightarrow \overline{p \vee q})$

and

(2) $(\overline{p \ \& \ q} \rightarrow \bar{p} \vee \bar{q}) \ \& \ (\bar{p} \vee \bar{q} \rightarrow \overline{p \ \& \ q})$

are provable in P.

Lemma 5. If $A_1, A_2, \ldots, A_n, B \vee C, B \vdash D$ and $A_1, A_2, \ldots, A_n, B \vee C, C \vdash D$, then $A_1, A_2, \ldots, A_n, B \vee C \vdash D$.

Proof: Supposing the $\vdash$-clauses in the antecedent of the Lemma, then, by the deduction theorem, $B \rightarrow D$ and $C \rightarrow D$ are yielded by the hypotheses A_i and $B \vee C$.

1. 1——1. n. $A_1, A_2, \ldots, A_n{}^\circ$
2. $B \vee C^\circ$
3. $B \rightarrow D$
4. $C \rightarrow D$
5. $(p \rightarrow r) \rightarrow ((q \rightarrow r) \rightarrow (p \vee q \rightarrow r))$

*6. $(B \rightarrow D) \rightarrow ((C \rightarrow D) \rightarrow (B \vee C \rightarrow D))$

*7. $B \vee C \rightarrow D$

8. D.

In this deduction, 5 is axiom V, 6 comes from 5 by substitution, 7 comes from 3, 4, and 6 by *modus ponens*, and 8 is 2, 7, mp.

Theorem 28. $\bar{p} \,\&\, \bar{q} \to \overline{p \vee q}$ is provable.

Proof: To simplify the proof, let V be any provable formula with no occurrences of p.

(3) $\bar{p} \,\&\, \bar{q},\ p \vee q,\ p \vdash q$,

for

1. $\bar{p} \,\&\, \bar{q}^{\circ}$
2. $p \vee q^{\circ}$
3. p°
4. $p \,\&\, q \to p$

*5. $\bar{p} \,\&\, \bar{q} \to \bar{p}$

6. $\bar{p}$
7. $p \to (q \to p \,\&\, q)$
8. $p \to (\bar{p} \to p \,\&\, \bar{p})$

*9. $p \,\&\, \bar{p}$

10. $p \,\&\, \bar{p} \to \bar{V}$
11. $\bar{V}$
12. $\bar{V} \to p$
13. $\bar{V} \to q$
14. q,

where 4 is axiom VI, 5 comes from 4 by substitution, 6 is 1, 5, mp, 7 is Ch. 8, Theorem 15, 8 is $S^{\bar{p}}_{q}(7)$, 9 comes from 3, 6, and 8 by *modus ponens*, 10 is Ch. 4, Theorem 13, 11 is 9, 10, mp, 12 is Ch. 4, Theorem 12, 13 is $S^{q}_{p}(12)$, and 14 is 11, 13, mp.

But also

(4) $\bar{p} \,\&\, \bar{q},\ p \vee q,\ q \vdash q$,

by Ch. 5, Definition 4 (*a*).

The application of Lemma 5 to (3) and (4) gives

(5) $\bar{p} \,\&\, \bar{q},\ p \vee q \vdash q$.

However,

(6) $\bar{p} \,\&\, \bar{q}, p \lor q \vdash \bar{q}$,

for $\bar{p} \,\&\, \bar{q}$ yields $\bar{q}$ by virtue of axiom VII.

The application of Ch. 8, Lemma 4 to (5) and (6) gives

(7) $\bar{p} \,\&\, \bar{q} \vdash \overline{p \lor q}$.

The theorem is obtainable by applying the deduction theorem to (7).

Theorem 29. $(\overline{p \lor q} \rightarrow \bar{p} \,\&\, \bar{q}) \,\&\, (\bar{p} \,\&\, \bar{q} \rightarrow \overline{p \lor q})$ is provable.

Proof: 1. $\overline{p \lor q} \rightarrow \bar{p} \,\&\, \bar{q}$

2. $\bar{p} \,\&\, \bar{q} \rightarrow \overline{p \lor q}$

3. $p \rightarrow (q \rightarrow p \,\&\, q)$

*4. $(\overline{p \lor q} \rightarrow \bar{p} \,\&\, \bar{q}) \rightarrow ((\bar{p} \,\&\, \bar{q} \rightarrow \overline{p \lor q}) \rightarrow$
$(\overline{p \lor q} \rightarrow \bar{p} \,\&\, \bar{q}) \,\&\, (\bar{p} \,\&\, \bar{q} \rightarrow \overline{p \lor q}))$

*5. $(\overline{p \lor q} \rightarrow \bar{p} \,\&\, \bar{q}) \,\&\, (\bar{p} \,\&\, \bar{q} \rightarrow \overline{p \lor q})$.

In this deduction, 1 is Ch. 4, Theorem 11, 2 is Theorem 28, 3 is Ch. 8, Theorem 1, 4 comes from 3 by substitution, and 5 comes from 1, 2, and 4 by *modus ponens*.

The next theorem is needed to facilitate the proof of Theorem 31.

Theorem 30. $(p \rightarrow q \,\&\, r) \rightarrow ((q \rightarrow s_1) \rightarrow ((r \rightarrow s_2) \rightarrow (p \rightarrow s_1 \,\&\, s_2)))$ is provable.

Proof: 1. $p \rightarrow q \,\&\, r^{\circ}$

2. $q \rightarrow s_1{}^{\circ}$

3. $r \rightarrow s_2{}^{\circ}$

4. p°

5. $q \,\&\, r$

*6. q

7. s_1

*8. r

9. s_2
10. $p \to (q \to p \,\&\, q)$
*11. $s_1 \to (s_2 \to s_1 \,\&\, s_2)$
*12. $s_1 \,\&\, s_2$.

In this deduction, 5 is 1, 4, mp, 6 comes from 5 by virtue of axiom VI, 7 is 2, 6, mp, 8 comes from 5 by virtue of axiom VII, 9 is 3, 8, mp, 10 is Ch. 8, Theorem 1, 11 comes from 10 by substitution, and 12 comes from 7, 9, and 11 by *modus ponens*. What this deduction shows is that

(8) $p \to q \,\&\, r,\ q \to s_1,\ r \to s_2,\ p \vdash s_1 \,\&\, s_2$.

The theorem is obtainable from four successive applications of the deduction theorem to (8).

Theorem 31. $\overline{p \,\&\, q} \to \bar{p} \lor \bar{q}$ is provable.

Proof: 1. $\overline{p \lor q} \to \bar{p} \,\&\, \bar{q}$
*2. $\overline{\bar{p} \lor \bar{q}} \to \bar{\bar{p}} \,\&\, \bar{\bar{q}}$
3. $(p \to q \,\&\, r) \to ((q \to s_1) \to ((r \to s_2) \to (p \to s_1 \,\&\, s_2)))$
*4. $(\overline{\bar{p} \lor \bar{q}} \to \bar{\bar{p}} \,\&\, \bar{\bar{q}}) \to ((\bar{\bar{p}} \to p) \to ((\bar{\bar{q}} \to q) \to (\overline{\bar{p} \lor \bar{q}} \to p \,\&\, q)))$
5. $\bar{\bar{p}} \to p$
6. $\bar{\bar{q}} \to q$
*7. $\overline{\bar{p} \lor \bar{q}} \to p \,\&\, q$
8. $(p \to q) \to (\bar{q} \to \bar{p})$
*9. $(\overline{\bar{p} \lor \bar{q}} \to p \,\&\, q) \to (\overline{p \,\&\, q} \to \overline{\overline{\bar{p} \lor \bar{q}}})$
10. $\overline{p \,\&\, q} \to \overline{\overline{\bar{p} \lor \bar{q}}}$
11. $\overline{\overline{\bar{p} \lor \bar{q}}} \to \bar{p} \lor \bar{q}$
12. $\overline{p \,\&\, q} \to \bar{p} \lor \bar{q}$.

In this deduction, 1 is Ch. 4, Theorem 11, 2 comes from 1 by substitution, 3 is Theorem 30, 4 comes from 3 by substitution, 5 is axiom XI, 6 is $S^{q}_{p}(5)$, 7 comes from 2, 4, 5, and 6 by *modus ponens*, 8 is axiom IX, 9 comes from 8 by substitution, 10 is 7, 9, mp, 11 is $S^{\bar{p} \vee \bar{q}}_{p}(5)$, and 12 is 10, 11, syll.

Theorem 32. $\bar{p} \vee \bar{q} \to \overline{p \,\&\, q}$ is provable.

Proof: To simplify the proof, let V be any provable formula with no occurrences of p.

(9) $p \,\&\, q, \bar{p} \vee \bar{q}, \bar{p} \vdash \bar{q}$,

for

1. $p \,\&\, q^{\circ}$
2. $\bar{p} \vee \bar{q}^{\circ}$
3. $\bar{p}^{\circ}$
4. $p \,\&\, q \to p$
5. p
6. $p \to (q \to p \,\&\, q)$
7. $p \to (\bar{p} \to p \,\&\, \bar{p})$

*8. $p \,\&\, \bar{p}$

9. $p \,\&\, \bar{p} \to \bar{V}$
10. $\bar{V}$
11. $\bar{V} \to p$
12. $\bar{V} \to \bar{q}$
13. $\bar{q}$,

where 4 is axiom VI, 5 is 1, 4, mp, 6 is Ch. 8, Theorem 15, 7 is $S^{\bar{p}}_{q}(6)$, 8 comes from 3, 5, and 7 by *modus ponens*, 9 is Ch. 4, Theorem 13, 10 is 8, 9, mp, 11 is Ch. 4, Theorem 12, 12 is $S^{\bar{q}}_{p}(11)$, and 13 is 10, 12, mp.

But also

(10) $p \,\&\, q, \bar{p} \vee \bar{q}, \bar{q} \vdash \bar{q}$,

by Ch. 5, Definition 4 (*a*).

The application of Lemma 5 to (9) and (10) gives

(11) $p \,\&\, q, \bar{p} \vee \bar{q} \vdash \bar{q}$.

However,

(12) $p \,\&\, q, p \vee \bar{q} \vdash q$,

for $p \,\&\, q$ yields q by virtue of axiom VII. If q is yielded by the hypotheses $p \,\&\, q$ and $\bar{p} \vee \bar{q}$ in that order, then q is yielded by the hypotheses $\bar{p} \vee \bar{q}$ and $p \,\&\, q$ in this latter order, for if a formula B is yielded by hypotheses A_i, then B is yielded by those hypotheses no matter in what order they are listed. (The order of the hypotheses is not mentioned in the definition of $\vdash$.) Therefore,

(13) $\bar{p} \vee \bar{q}, p \,\&\, q \vdash q$

and

(14) $\bar{p} \vee \bar{q}, p \,\&\, q \vdash \bar{q}$,

by (12) and (11) respectively.

The application of Ch. 8, Lemma 4 to (13) and (14) gives

(15) $\bar{p} \vee \bar{q} \vdash \overline{p \,\&\, q}$.

The theorem is obtainable by applying the deduction theorem to (15).

Theorem 33. $(\overline{p \,\&\, q} \rightarrow \bar{p} \vee \bar{q}) \,\&\, (\bar{p} \vee \bar{q} \rightarrow \overline{p \,\&\, q})$ is provable.

Proof:
1. $\overline{p \,\&\, q} \rightarrow \bar{p} \vee \bar{q}$
2. $\bar{p} \vee \bar{q} \rightarrow \overline{p \,\&\, q}$
3. $p \rightarrow (q \rightarrow p \,\&\, q)$

*4. $(\overline{p \,\&\, q} \rightarrow \bar{p} \vee \bar{q}) \rightarrow ((\bar{p} \vee \bar{q} \rightarrow \overline{p \,\&\, q}) \rightarrow (\overline{p \,\&\, q} \rightarrow \bar{p} \vee \bar{q}) \,\&\, (\bar{p} \vee \bar{q} \rightarrow \overline{p \,\&\, q})$

*5. $(\overline{p \,\&\, q} \rightarrow \bar{p} \vee \bar{q}) \,\&\, (\bar{p} \vee \bar{q} \rightarrow \overline{p \,\&\, q})$.

Negations of Disjunctions and Conjunctions

In this deduction, 1 is Theorem 31, 2 is Theorem 32, 3 is Ch. 8, Theorem 15, 4 comes from 3 by substitution, and 5 comes from 1, 2, and 4 by *modus ponens*.

Note. Theorems 29 and 33 are frequently referred to in the literature as De Morgan's Laws.

Chapter Ten

EQUIVALENCE

A formula of the form $(A \rightarrow B)$ & $(B \rightarrow A)$ will be written, for the sake of convenient brevity, as $A \sim B$. The sign $\sim$, called the sign of *equivalence*, is not, of course, a sign in P; it belongs to the languages used for talking about P. An expression, of the form $A \sim B$, which contains $\sim$ is, therefore, not itself a formula but is an abbreviative expression for a formula.

Two formulae A and B for which it is true that

(1) $A \sim B$ is provable

are called *equivalent* (to one another).

Theorem 34. $p \sim \bar{\bar{p}}$ is provable.

Proof: 1. $p \rightarrow \bar{\bar{p}}$

2. $\bar{\bar{p}} \rightarrow p$

3. $p \rightarrow (q \rightarrow p \;\&\; q)$

*4. $(p \rightarrow \bar{\bar{p}}) \rightarrow ((\bar{\bar{p}} \rightarrow p) \rightarrow (p \rightarrow \bar{\bar{p}}) \;\&\; (\bar{\bar{p}} \rightarrow p))$

*5. $(p \rightarrow \bar{\bar{p}}) \;\&\; (\bar{\bar{p}} \rightarrow p)$

6. $p \sim \bar{\bar{p}}$.

In this deduction, 1 is axiom X, 2 is axiom XI, 3 is Ch. 8, Theorem 15, 4 comes from 3 by substitution, 5 comes from 1, 2, and 4 by *modus ponens*, and 6 is 5.

Theorem 35. $(p \sim q) \rightarrow (q \sim p)$ is provable.

Proof: 1. $q \,\&\, p \rightarrow p \,\&\, q$

*2. $(p \rightarrow q) \,\&\, (q \rightarrow p) \rightarrow (q \rightarrow p) \,\&\, (p \rightarrow q)$

3. $(p \sim q) \rightarrow (q \sim p)$.

In this deduction, 1 is Ch. 4, Theorem 4, 2 comes from 1 by substitution, and 3 is 2.

Theorem 36. If A and B are provable, then A and B are equivalent.

Proof: Suppose A and B are provable.

1. A
2. B
3. $p \rightarrow (q \rightarrow p)$

*4. $B \rightarrow (A \rightarrow B)$

5. $A \rightarrow B$

*6. $A \rightarrow (B \rightarrow A)$

7. $B \rightarrow A$
8. $p \rightarrow (q \rightarrow p \,\&\, q)$

*9. $(A \rightarrow B) \rightarrow ((B \rightarrow A) \rightarrow (A \sim B))$

*10. $A \sim B$.

In this deduction, 3 is axiom I, 4 comes from 3 by substitution, 5 is 2, 4, mp, 6 comes from 3 by substitution, 7 is 1, 6, mp, 8 is Ch. 8, Theorem 15, 9 comes from 8 by substitution, and 10 comes from 5, 7, and 9 by *modus ponens*.

Theorem 37. If A is equivalent to B and B is equivalent to C, then A is equivalent to C.

Proof: Suppose A is equivalent to B and B to C.

1. $A \sim B$
2. $B \sim C$

*3. $A \rightarrow B$

*4. $B \rightarrow C$

5. $A \rightarrow C$

*6. $B \rightarrow A$

*7. $C \to B$
8. $C \to A$
9. $p \to (q \to p \,\&\, q)$
*10. $(A \to C) \to ((C \to A) \to (A \sim C))$
*11. $A \sim C$.

In this deduction, 3 comes from 1 by virtue of axiom VI, 4 comes from 2 by virtue of axiom VI, 5 is 3, 4, syll, 6 comes from 1 by virtue of axiom VII, 7 comes from 2 by virtue of axiom VII, 8 is 6, 7, syll, 9 is Ch. 8, Theorem 15, 10 comes from 9 by substitution, and 11 comes from 5, 8, and 10 by *modus ponens*.

If D designates a propositional variable, we write $A(D)$ when we wish to make explicit that A contains some occurrence of D; we then write $A(B)$ instead of $S^B_D(A)$.

Theorem 38. If D is a propositional variable that occurs in A and B is equivalent to C, then $A(B)$ is equivalent to $A(C)$.

Proof: We proceed by course-of-values induction on the number $k(=0$ or 1 or 2 or $\ldots)$ of occurrences of connectives in A. Accordingly, we must first prove

$T(0)$: If D is a propositional variable that occurs in A and B is equivalent to C, then, if there are no occurrences of connectives in A, $A(B)$ is equivalent to $A(C)$.

Suppose that D is a propositional variable and that $\vdash B \sim C$. If there are no occurrences of connectives in $A(D)$, A must be (i.e., designate) a propositional variable. Since D occurs in A, A must be D. Then $A(B)$ is B and $A(C)$ is C. From the supposition that $\vdash B \sim C$ it follows that $A(B)$ is equivalent to $A(C)$.

Thus, it has been shown that $T(0)$ is true.

Next, we wish to establish that if $T(k \leq m)$ is true,

then $T(m+1)$ is true, k and m being any non-negative whole numbers. Therefore, we suppose

$T(k \leq m)$: If D is a propositional variable that occurs in A and B is equivalent to C, then, if there are not more than m occurrences of connectives in A, $A(B)$ is equivalent to $A(C)$,

and attempt to derive as conclusion the truth of

$T(m+1)$: If D is a propositional variable that occurs in A and B is equivalent to C, then, if there are $m+1$ occurrences of connectives in A, $A(B)$ is equivalent to $A(C)$.

Suppose that D is a propositional variable and that $\vdash B \sim C$. Let there be $m+1$ occurrences of connectives in $A(D)$, so the form of A is either (*a*) $\overline{E}$, or (*b*) $E_1 \vee E_2$, or (*c*) $E_1 \,\&\, E_2$, or (*d*) $E_1 \rightarrow E_2$. (A convenient way of referring to these alternatives is to say that $-$, $\vee$, &, and $\rightarrow$, respectively, is the *principal* connective.)

(*a*) If $A(D)$ is $\overline{E}$, then D occurs in E, so E is $E(D)$ and A is $\overline{E(D)}$. Also, E cannot contain more than m occurrences of connectives. Therefore, by $T(k \leq m)$, $E(B)$ is equivalent to $E(C)$. Now, if any two formulae E_1 and E_2 are equivalent, then their negations are equivalent; for suppose that E_1 and E_2 are equivalent:

1. $E_1 \sim E_2$
*2. $E_1 \rightarrow E_2$
*3. $\overline{E}_2 \rightarrow \overline{E}_1$
*4. $E_2 \rightarrow E_1$
*5. $\overline{E}_1 \rightarrow \overline{E}_2$
6. $p \rightarrow (q \rightarrow p \,\&\, q)$
*7. $(\overline{E}_1 \rightarrow \overline{E}_2) \rightarrow ((\overline{E}_2 \rightarrow \overline{E}_1) \rightarrow (\overline{E}_1 \sim \overline{E}_2))$
*8. $\overline{E}_1 \sim \overline{E}_2$.

In this deduction, 2 comes from 1 by virtue of axiom

VI, 3 comes from 2 by virtue of axiom IX, 4 comes from 1 by virtue of axiom VII, 5 comes from 4 by virtue of axiom IX, 6 is Ch. 8, Theorem 15, 7 comes from 6 by substitution, and 8 comes from 3, 5, and 7 by *modus ponens*. Accordingly, $\overline{E(B)}$ is equivalent to $\overline{E(C)}$, that is $A(B)$ is equivalent to $A(C)$.

(*b*) If $A(D)$ is $E_1 \vee E_2$, then D occurs in $E_1 \vee E_2$. D occurs in either (i) E_1 only, or (ii) E_2 only, or (iii) both E_1 and E_2.

(i) If D occurs only in E_1, then $A(D)$ is $E_1(D) \vee E_2$. Since E_1 cannot contain more than m occurrences of connectives, then, by $T(k \leq m)$, $E_1(B)$ is equivalent to $E_1(C)$. We next show that

(2) $p \rightarrow q, p \vee r \vdash q \vee r$.

(3) $p \rightarrow q, p \vee r, p \vdash q \vee r$,

for the hypotheses p and $p \rightarrow q$ yield q, by *modus ponens*, and $q \vee r$ is obtainable from q by virtue of axiom III.

(4) $p \rightarrow q, p \vee r, r \vdash q \vee r$,

for $q \vee r$ is obtainable from the hypothesis r by virtue of axiom IV. (2) follows from (3) and (4), by Ch. 9, Lemma 5.

Applying the deduction theorem to (2) gives

(5) $\vdash (p \rightarrow q) \rightarrow (p \vee r \rightarrow q \vee r)$.

Now, if E_3, E_4, and A_1 are any formulae, then if E_3 and E_4 are equivalent, $E_3 \vee A_1$ and $E_4 \vee A_1$ are equivalent; for suppose that E_3 and E_4 are equivalent:

1. $E_3 \sim E_4$
*2. $E_3 \rightarrow E_4$
3. $(p \rightarrow q) \rightarrow (p \vee r \rightarrow q \vee r)$
*4. $(E_3 \rightarrow E_4) \rightarrow (E_3 \vee A_1 \rightarrow E_4 \vee A_1)$
5. $E_3 \vee A_1 \rightarrow E_4 \vee A_1$
*6. $E_4 \rightarrow E_3$
*7. $(E_4 \rightarrow E_3) \rightarrow (E_4 \vee A_1 \rightarrow E_3 \vee A_1)$
8. $E_4 \vee A_1 \rightarrow E_3 \vee A_1$

9. $p \to (q \to p \ \& \ q)$

*10. $(E_3 \vee A_1 \to E_4 \vee A_1) \to ((E_4 \vee A_1 \to E_3 \vee A_1) \to ((E_3 \vee A_1) \sim (E_4 \vee A_1)))$

*11. $(E_3 \vee A_1) \sim (E_4 \vee A)$.

In this deduction, 2 comes from 1 by virtue of axiom VI, 3 is the formula in (5), 4 comes from 3 by substitution, 5 is 2, 4, mp, 6 comes from 1 by virtue of axiom VII, 7 comes from 3 by substitution, 8 is 6, 7, mp, 9 is Ch. 8, Theorem 15, 10 comes from 9 by substitution, and 11 comes from 5, 8, and 10 by *modus ponens*.

Since $E_1(B)$ is equivalent to $E_1(C)$, it follows, by the result just proved, that $E_1(B) \vee E_2$ is equivalent to $E_1(C) \vee E_2$, that is $A(B)$ is equivalent to $A(C)$.

(ii) If D occurs only in E_2, then it may be shown in a way similar to that pursued in (i) that $A(B)$ is equivalent to $A(C)$; this time, however, one first establishes (by Ch. 9, Lemma 5) that

(6) $p \to q, r \vee p \vdash r \vee q$,

so that

(7) $\vdash (p \to q) \to (r \vee p \to r \vee q)$,

using this to obtain finally that $E_1 \vee E_2(B)$ is equivalent to $E_1 \vee E_2(C)$.

(iii) If D occurs in E_1 and E_2, then $A(D)$ is $E_1(D) \vee E_2(D)$. Since neither E_1 nor E_2 can contain more than m occurrences of connectives, $E_1(B)$ is equivalent to $E_1(C)$ and $E_2(B)$ is equivalent to $E_2(C)$, by $T(k \leq m)$. Next, we show that

(8) $p \to q, r \to s, p \vee r \vdash q \vee s$.

(9) $p \to q, r \to s, p \vee r, p \vdash q \vee s$,

for the hypotheses p and $p \to q$ yield q, and $q \vee s$ is obtainable from q.

(10) $p \to q, r \to s, p \vee r, r \vdash q \vee s$,

for the hypotheses r and $r \to s$ yield s, and $q \vee s$ is obtainable from s. (8) follows from (9) and (10), by Ch. 9, Lemma 5.

Applying the deduction theorem to (8) gives

(11) $\vdash (p \to q) \to ((r \to s) \to (p \vee r \to q \vee s))$.

If A_1, A_2, B_1, and B_2 are any formulae such that A_1 is equivalent to B_1 and A_2 is equivalent to B_2, then $A_1 \vee A_2$ is equivalent to $B_1 \vee B_2$; for suppose that A_1 and B_1, and A_2 and B_2, are equivalent:

1. $A_1 \sim B_1$
2. $A_2 \sim B_2$

*3. $A_1 \to B_1$

*4. $A_2 \to B_2$

5. $(p \to q) \to ((r \to s) \to (p \vee r \to q \vee s))$

*6. $(A_1 \to B_1) \to ((A_2 \to B_2) \to (A_1 \vee A_2 \to B_1 \vee B_2))$

*7. $A_1 \vee A_2 \to B_1 \vee B_2$

*8. $B_1 \to A_1$

*9. $B_2 \to A_2$

*10. $(B_1 \to A_1) \to ((B_2 \to A_2) \to (B_1 \vee B_2 \to A_1 \vee A_2))$

*11. $B_1 \vee B_2 \to A_1 \vee A_2$

12. $p \to (q \to p \ \& \ q)$

*13. $(A_1 \vee A_2 \to B_1 \vee B_2) \to ((B_1 \vee B_2 \to A_1 \vee A_2) \to ((A_1 \vee A_2) \sim (B_1 \vee B_2)))$

*14. $(A_1 \vee A_2) \sim (B_1 \vee B_2)$.

In this deduction, 3 comes from 1 by virtue of axiom VI, 4 comes from 2 by virtue of that axiom, 5 is the formula in (11), 6 comes from 5 by substitution, 7 comes from 3, 4, and 6 by *modus ponens*, 8 comes from 1 by virtue of axiom VII, 9 comes from 2 by virtue of that axiom, 10 comes from 5 by substitution, 11 comes from 8, 9, and 10 by *modus ponens*, 12 is Ch. 8, Theorem 15, 13 comes from 12 by substitution, and 14 comes from 7, 11, and 13 by *modus ponens*.

Since $E_1(B)$ is equivalent to $E_1(C)$ and $E_2(B)$ is equivalent to $E_2(C)$, it follows, by the result just proved, that $E_1(B) \vee E_2(B)$ is equivalent to $E_1(C) \vee E_2(C)$, that is $A(B)$ is equivalent to $A(C)$.

(c) If $A(D)$ is E_1 & E_2, then D occurs in E_1 & E_2. D occurs in either (i) E_1 only, or (ii) E_2 only, or (iii) both E_1 and E_2.

(i) If D occurs only in E_1, then $A(D)$ is $E_1(D)$ & E_2. Since E_1 cannot contain more than m occurrences of connectives, then, by $T(k \leqq m)$, $E_1(B)$ is equivalent to $E_1(C)$. Next, we show that

(12) $p \to q, p \,\&\, r \vdash q \,\&\, r.$

$p \,\&\, r$ yields p, which with $p \to q$ produces q; also, $p \,\&\, r$ yields r, so the hypotheses yield q and r and therefore, by Ch. 8, Theorem 15, yield $q \,\&\, r$.

Applying the deduction theorem to (12) gives

(13) $\vdash (p \to q) \to (p \,\&\, r \to q \,\&\, r).$

Now, if two formulae E_3 and E_4 are equivalent, then E_3 & A_1 is equivalent to E_4 & A_1; for suppose E_3 is equivalent to E_4:

1. $E_3 \sim E_4$
*2. $E_3 \to E_4$
3. $(p \to q) \to (p \,\&\, r \to q \,\&\, r)$
*4. $(E_3 \to E_4) \to (E_3 \,\&\, A_1 \to E_4 \,\&\, A_1)$
5. $E_3 \,\&\, A_1 \to E_4 \,\&\, A_1$
*6. $E_4 \to E_3$
*7. $(E_4 \to E_3) \to (E_4 \,\&\, A_1 \to E_3 \,\&\, A_1)$
8. $E_4 \,\&\, A_1 \to E_3 \,\&\, A_1$
9. $p \to (q \to p \,\&\, q)$
*10. $(E_3 \,\&\, A_1 \to E_4 \,\&\, A_1) \to ((E_4 \,\&\, A_1 \to$
$E_3 \,\&\, A_1) \to ((E_3 \,\&\, A_1) \sim (E_4 \,\&\, A_1)))$
*11. $(E_3 \,\&\, A_1) \sim (E_4 \,\&\, A_1)$.

In this deduction, 2 comes from 1 by virtue of axiom VI, 3 is the formula in (13), 4 comes from 3 by substitution, 5 is 2, 4, mp, 6 comes from 1 by virtue of axiom VII, 7 comes from 3 by substitution, 8 is 6, 7, mp, 9 is Ch. 8, Theorem 15, 10 comes from 9 by substitution, and 11 comes from 5, 8, and 10 by *modus ponens*.

Since $E_1(B)$ is equivalent to $E_1(C)$, then, by the

result just proved, $E_1(B)$ & E_2 is equivalent to $E_1(C)$ & E_2, that is $A(B)$ is equivalent to $A(C)$.

(ii) If D occurs only in E_2, then it may be shown in a way similar to that pursued in (i) that $A(B)$ is equivalent to $A(C)$; this time, however, one first establishes that

(14) $p \to q, r \,\&\, p \vdash r \,\&\, q$,

so that

(15) $\vdash (p \to q) \to (r \,\&\, p \to r \,\&\, q)$,

using this to obtain finally that E_1 & $E_2(B)$ is equivalent to E_1 & $E_2(C)$.

(iii) If D occurs in E_1 and E_2, then $A(D)$ is $E_1(D)$ & $E_2(D)$. Since neither E_1 nor E_2 can contain more than m occurrences of connectives, it follows, by $T(k \leq m)$, that $E_1(B)$ is equivalent to $E_1(C)$ and that $E_2(B)$ is equivalent to $E_2(C)$. Next, we show that

(16) $p \to q, r \to s, p \,\&\, r \vdash q \,\&\, s$.

The hypothesis p & r yields p, which with $p \to s$ enables us to deduce s. Also, p & r yields r, which with $r \to s$ enables us to deduce s. Having q and s, we can get q & s by applying Ch. 8, Theorem 15. Applying the deduction theorem to (16) gives

(17) $\vdash (p \to q) \to ((r \to s) \to (p \,\&\, r \to q \,\&\, s))$.

If A_1 is equivalent to B_1 and A_2 to B_2, then A_1 & A_2 is equivalent to B_1 & B_2; for suppose that A_1 and B_1, and A_2 and B_2, are equivalent:

1. $A_1 \sim B_1$
2. $A_2 \sim B_2$

*3. $A_1 \to B_1$

*4. $A_2 \to B_2$

5. $(p \to q) \to ((r \to s) \to (p \,\&\, r \to q \,\&\, s))$

*6. $(A_1 \to B_1) \to ((A_2 \to B_2) \to (A_1 \,\&\, A_2 \to B_1 \,\&\, B_2))$

*7. $A_1 \,\&\, A_2 \to B_1 \,\&\, B_2$

*8. $B_1 \to A_1$

$*9.\ B_2 \to A_2$

$*10.\ (B_1 \to A_1) \to ((B_2 \to A_2) \to (B_1 \ \&\ B_2 \to A_1 \ \&\ A_2))$

$*11.\ B_1 \ \&\ B_2 \to A_1 \ \&\ A_2$

$12.\ p \to (q \to p \ \&\ q)$

$*13.\ (A_1 \ \&\ A_2 \to B_1 \ \&\ B_2) \to ((B_1 \ \&\ B_2 \to A_1 \ \&\ A_2) \to ((A_1 \ \&\ A_2) \sim (B_1 \ \&\ B_2)))$

$*14.\ (A_1 \ \&\ A_2) \sim (B_1 \ \&\ B_2).$

In this deduction, 3 comes from 1 by virtue of axiom VI, 4 comes from 2 by virtue of that axiom, 5 is the formula in (17), 6 comes from 5 by substitution, 7 comes from 3, 4, and 6 by *modus ponens*. 8 comes from 1 by virtue of axiom VII, 9 comes from 2 by virtue of that axiom, 10 comes from 5 by substitution, 11 comes from 8, 9, and 10 by *modus ponens*, 12 is Ch. 8, Theorem 15, 13 comes from 12 by substitution, and 14 comes from 7, 11, and 13 by *modus ponens*.

Since $E_1(B)$ is equivalent to $E_1(C)$ and $E_2(B)$ is equivalent to $E_2(C)$, it follows, by the result just proved, that $E_1(B) \ \&\ E_2(B)$ is equivalent to $E_1(C) \ \&\ E_2(C)$, that is $A(B)$ is equivalent to $A(C)$.

(*d*) If $A(D)$ is $E_1 \to E_2$, then D occurs in $E_1 \to E_2$. D occurs in either (i) E_1 only, or (ii) E_2 only, or (iii) both E_1 and E_2.

(i) If D occurs only in E_1, then $A(D)$ is $E_1(D) \to E_2$. Since E_1 cannot contain more than m occurrences of connectives, it follows, by $T(k \leq m)$, that $E_1(B)$ is equivalent to $E_1(C)$.

(18) $p \sim q, p \to r, q \vdash r,$

for the hypotheses $p \sim q$ and q yield p, while p and $p \to r$ produce r; again,

(19) $p \sim q, q \to r, p \vdash r,$

for $p \sim q$ and p yield q, while q and $q \to r$ produce r. Applying to (18) and (19) first the deduction theorem and then Ch. 8, Theorem 15, we obtain

(20) $p \sim q \vdash (p \to r) \sim (q \to r)$,

so

(21) $\vdash (p \sim q) \to ((p \to r) \sim (q \to r))$.

Since $E_1(B)$ is equivalent to $E_1(C)$, it follows, by (21), that $E_1(B) \to E_2$ is equivalent to $E_1(C) \to E_2$, that is $A(B)$ is equivalent to $A(C)$.

(ii) If D occurs only in E_2, then it may be shown in a way similar to that pursued in (i) that $A(B)$ is equivalent to $A(C)$; this time, however, one first establishes that

(22) $p \sim q, r \to p, r \vdash q$

and

(23) $p \sim q, r \to q, r \vdash p$,

so that, by the deduction theorem and Ch. 8, Theorem 15,

(24) $\vdash (p \sim q) \to ((r \to p) \sim (r \to q))$;

one uses this to obtain finally that $E_1 \to E_2(B)$ is equivalent to $E_1 \to E_2(C)$.

(iii) If D occurs in E_1 and E_2, then $A(D)$ is $E_1(D) \to E_2(D)$. Since neither E_1 nor E_2 can contain more than m occurrences of connectives, it follows, by $T(k \leq m)$, that $E_1(B)$ is equivalent to $E_1(C)$ and that $E_2(B)$ is equivalent to $E_2(C)$.

(25) $p \sim q, r \sim s, p \to r, q \vdash s$,

for q and $p \sim q$ yield p; p and $p \to r$ produce r; and r and $r \sim s$ produce s; again,

(26) $p \sim q, r \sim s, q \to s, p \vdash r$,

for p and $p \sim q$ yield q; q and $q \to s$ produce s; and s and $r \sim s$ produce r. By the deduction theorem and Ch. 8, Theorem 15 applied to (25) and (26) we obtain

(27) $\vdash (p \sim q) \to ((r \sim s) \to ((p \to r) \sim (q \to s)))$.

Since $E_1(B)$ and $E_1(C)$, and $E_2(B)$ and $E_2(C)$, are equivalent, it follows, by (27), that $E_1(B) \to E_2(B)$ and $E_1(C) \to E_2(C)$ are equivalent, that is $A(B)$ is equivalent to $A(C)$.

This completes the proof of Theorem 38.

Theorem 38 says that if a propositional variable D occurs in A, then $S_D^B(A)$ and $S_D^C(A)$ are equivalent if B and C are equivalent. But, in fact, the weaker

Theorem 39. If a propositional variable D occurs in A and B is equivalent to C, then E_1 and E_2 are equivalent, where E_1, is a formula which is the same as $A(D)$ except that at least one (but not necessarily every) occurrence of D is replaced by an occurrence of B and E_2 is a formula which is the same as E_1 except that C occurs in E_2 wherever and only wherever B occurs in E_1 ——

is permitted and justified by the proof of Theorem 38; for nothing in that proof depends on every occurrence of D, but only on some occurrence of D, being replaced by B and C, provided that just the occurrences of D that are replaced by B are also replaced by C.

For example, let $A(p)$ be

(28) $p \rightarrow p \vee q$.

Since provable formulae are equivalent (Theorem 36), $\vdash A(p \rightarrow V) \sim A(p \rightarrow p)$:

(29) $\vdash ((p \rightarrow V) \rightarrow (p \rightarrow V) \vee q) \sim ((p \rightarrow p) \rightarrow (p \rightarrow p) \vee q)$,

by Theorem 38; and

(30) $\vdash (p \rightarrow (p \rightarrow V) \vee q) \sim (p \rightarrow (p \rightarrow p) \vee q)$,

by Theorem 39.

Chapter Eleven

CONSISTENCY

The letters p, q, r, etc. have been called propositional variables. This suggests that they represent any propositions. And this is certainly one legitimate interpretation of them. But it is not the only one that is legitimate. For example, they may be given the rather wider significance of representing both any propositions and any propositional functions, the latter being statements such as 'x is human' and 'if x is divisible by y and y is divisible by z, then x is divisible by z'—statements containing letters which indicate the presence of blank places to be filled in by names of individual objects.

Any particular object that is represented by a variable is called a *value* of the variable. We shall now interpret the propositional variables as variables having two and only two values, t and f. These letters may be regarded as names of The True and The False respectively. In order that compound formulae may also have the values t and f we lay down the following definitions:

I. $\bar{t}=f \quad \bar{f}=t;$

II. $t \vee t=t \quad t \vee f=t \quad f \vee t=t \quad f \vee f=f;$

III. $t \,\&\, t=t \quad t \,\&\, f=f \quad f \,\&\, t=f \quad f \,\&\, f=f;$

IV. $t \rightarrow t=t \quad t \rightarrow f=f \quad f \rightarrow t=t \quad f \rightarrow f=t.$

These four groups of equalities will be referred to as the *standard valuation tables*. (Another common name for them is *truth tables*.)

For example, if p and q in

(1) $p \rightarrow (\bar{q} \vee p \,\&\, q)$

have the values f and t respectively, then (1) becomes in turn, by the standard valuation tables,

(2) $f \rightarrow (\bar{t} \vee f \,\&\, t)$,

(3) $f \rightarrow f \vee f$,

since $\bar{t}=f$ and $f \,\&\, t=f$,

(4) $f \rightarrow f$,

since $f \vee f=f$,

(5) t,

since $f \rightarrow f=t$. Thus, (1) has the value t when the value of p is f and the value of q is t.

A formula that always has the value t no matter what combination of values is assigned to its component propositional variables is called a *t-formula*, while one that always has the value f is called a *f-formula*. (A t-formula is often called a *tautology* in Anglo-American literature on logic.) It must be emphasized that a formula is a t-formula, and similarly a f-formula, relatively to the standard valuation tables. A formula that always has the value t when the valuation is carried out by reference to the standard tables might not always have the value t when the valuation is carried out by reference to valuation tables other than the standard ones.

Theorem 40. Each axiom of P is a t-formula.

Proof: We shall show the theorem to be true for axioms I and II, leaving the other cases to the reader.

For axiom I, there are four combinations of values to be considered: both p and q have the value t; p has the value t and q the value f, and *vice versa*; and both p and q have the value f. These possibilities lead to the following four lines, where the standard valuation tables have been used to establish the equalities:

(6) $t \to (t \to t) = t \to t = t$;
(7) $t \to (f \to t) = t \to t = t$;
(8) $f \to (t \to f) = f \to f = t$;
(9) $f \to (f \to f) = f \to t = t$.

For axiom II, there are eight combinations of values to be considered: each of p, q, and r has the value t; p and q have the value t and r has the value f; p and r have the value t and q has the value f; p has the value t and q and r have the value f; p has the value f and q and r have the value t; p and r have the value f and q has the value t; p and q have the value f and r has the value t; and, finally, each of p, q, and r has the value f. These possibilities lead to the following eight lines:

(10) $(t \to (t \to t)) \to ((t \to t) \to (t \to t)) = (t \to t) \to (t \to t) =$
$t \to t = t$;
(11) $(t \to (t \to f)) \to ((t \to t) \to (t \to f)) = (t \to f) \to (t \to f) =$
$f \to f = t$;
(12) $(t \to (f \to t)) \to ((t \to f) \to (t \to t) = (t \to t) \to (f \to t) =$
$t \to t = t$;
(13) $(t \to (f \to f)) \to ((t \to f) \to (t \to f) = (t \to t) \to (f \to f) =$
$t \to t = t$;
(14) $(f \to (t \to t)) \to ((f \to t) \to (f \to t)) = (f \to t) \to (t \to t) =$
$t \to t = t$;
(15) $(f \to (t \to f)) \to ((f \to t) \to (f \to f)) = (f \to f) \to (t \to t) =$
$t \to t = t$;
(16) $(f \to (f \to t)) \to ((f \to f) \to (f \to t)) = (f \to t) \to (t \to t) =$
$t \to t = t$;
(17) $(f \to (f \to f)) \to ((f \to f) \to (f \to f) = (f \to t) \to (t \to t) =$
$t \to t = t$.

Theorem 41. If A is a provable t-formula and B is deduced from A by the rule of substitution, then B is a t-formula.

Proof: If A is a provable t-formula, it has the value t no matter what value the propositional variable D, which is substituted for in the deduction of B from A, has; therefore, if B is $S_D^C(A)$, B is a t-formula, for C's having the value t is tantamount to D's having the value t in A, while C's having the value f is tantamount to D's having the value f in A.

Theorem 42. If A is a provable t-formula and $A \rightarrow B$ is a provable t-formula, then B is a t-formula.

Proof: If A and $A \rightarrow B$ are provable t-formulae, they always have the value t; therefore, $t \rightarrow B$ always has the value t, so it is impossible for B to have the value f at all, for if it did have the value f the result would be that $t \rightarrow f$ would have the value t, and this is incompatible with the definition that $t \rightarrow f$ has the value f.

Theorem 43. If A is provable, then A is a t-formula.

Proof: A being any provable formula, consider any particular proof of it from the axioms, using the two rules of deduction, namely the rule of substitution and the rule of *modus ponens*. If A is the very first step of the proof, A must be an axiom. By Theorem 40, A is a t-formula. Suppose next that the theorem is true for any proof of a formula A in which A occurs as the step numbered k where $k \leq m$. Now, if a formula A occurs in a proof as the step numbered $m+1$, then either (a) A is an axiom, or (b) it is deduced from a preceding step by the rule of substitution, or (c) it is deduced from two preceding steps by the rule of *modus ponens*. If (a), then A is a t-formula, by Theorem 40. If (b), then A is a t-formula by the supposition of $T(k \leq m)$ and Theorem 41. If (c), then A is a t-formula by the supposition of $T(k \leq m)$ and Theorem 42.

Theorem 44. There is no formula A such that both A and $\bar{A}$ are provable.

Proof: If A is provable then, by Theorem 43, A is a t-formula. Hence, by the standard valuation table for negation, $\bar{A}$ must be a f-formula. However, if $\bar{A}$ is also provable, then, by Theorem 43, $\bar{A}$ is a t-formula. Thus, if some formula A and its negation $\bar{A}$ were both provable, $\bar{A}$ would be simultaneously a t-formula and a f-formula; but this is impossible, since the properties of being a t-formula and being a f-formula are mutually exclusive. We must therefore deny that there is some formula A such that both it and its negation are provable.

A system that contains negation and which is such that there is no formula A of the system of which it is true to say: 'A is provable in the system and the contradictory $\bar{A}$ of A is provable in the system'—is said to be *free from contradiction* or *consistent*. Thus, by Theorem 44, P is free from contradiction.

A system which is such that not each of its formulae is provable in it is said to be *absolutely consistent*. When this notation of consistency is being considered, the type of consistency referred to in the previous paragraph is often called *relative* or *simple consistency*. P is absolutely consistent, because the negations of its provable formulae, such as $p \to p$ and $p \vee \bar{p}$, are not provable; if they were provable, P would not be free from contradiction. Hence,

Theorem 45. P is absolutely consistent.

Chapter Twelve

INDEPENDENCE

None of the eleven axioms of P is redundant, for none of them can be deduced from the others. In short, each of our axioms is *independent*. The purpose of the present chapter is to demonstrate how this assertion of independence can be justified.

Let us begin by considering a particular axiom, say axiom VI ($p \ \& \ q \rightarrow p$). Our intention is to construct a set of conditions under which each of the other axioms and each formula deducible from them has a certain property, this property, however, not being possessed by axiom VI; so that axiom VI cannot be deducible from the other axioms. The set of conditions to be constructed is allied to the definitions incorporated in the standard valuation tables of Ch. 11.

We regard the propositional variables as variables having two possible values, which we shall label J and K. In order that compound formulae may also have these values, we lay down valuation definitions for each of the four connectives $-$, $\vee$, $\&$, and $\rightarrow$. The definitions for $-$, $\vee$, and $\rightarrow$ are exactly the same as the definitions in I, II, and IV of Ch. 11 except that J replaces t and K replaces f. The definition for $\&$ is changed to

(1) $J \ \& \ J=J \quad J \ \& \ K=K \quad K \ \& \ J=J, \quad K \ \& \ K=K$

which can be expressed briefly as

(2) $A \ \& \ B=B$.

Under the described conditions, each axiom other than

axiom VI is a J-formula, that is it always has the value J. Since J corresponds to t and K to f, this assertion is justified with respect to axioms I–V and IX–XI by Ch. 11, Theorem 40. Only the valuation table for & has been essentially altered, so that only the axioms containing & might have the value K. We shall show that axioms VII and VIII do not, in fact, have the value K, while axiom VI does have the value K for some values of the component propositional variables.

If axiom VII were to have the value K, then, by the table for $\rightarrow$, $p \,\&\, q=J$ and $q=K$; but this impossible by (2), for if q has the value K, $p \,\&\, q$ must also have the value K, not the value J.

If axiom VIII were to have the value K, then, by the table for $\rightarrow$, $r \rightarrow p=J$ and $((r \rightarrow q) \rightarrow (r \rightarrow p \,\&\, q))=K$; from the latter it follows that $r \rightarrow q=J$ and $r \rightarrow p \,\&\, q=K$, by the table for $\rightarrow$; again by that table, since $r \rightarrow p \,\&\, q=K$, $r=J$ and $p \,\&\, q=K$. From this last equality it follows, by (2), that $q=K$. It has already been established that $r \rightarrow q=J$; but this is impossible, since it has also been established that $r=J$ and $q=K$.

On the other hand, axiom VI has the value K for some values of its variables: when $p=K$ and $q=J$, $K \,\&\, J \rightarrow K$ has the value, by (2), of $J \rightarrow K$, which in turn has the value K, by the table for $\rightarrow$.

Similarly to the proofs of Ch. 11, Theorems 41 and 42, proofs may be given that any formula derived by substitution from a J-formula is a J-formula and that any formula derived by *modus ponens* from two J-formulae is a J-formula. Therefore, any formula deduced from axioms I–V and VII–XI is a J-formula. Since axiom VI is not a J-formula, it follows that it cannot be deduced from the other axioms. Hence, axiom VI is independent.

More generally, to prove the independence of each of

the axioms III–XI, we regard the propositional variables as having two possible values J and K, and we lay down valuation definitions for the connectives. Subject to a qualification, these definitions for the connectives are the same as those in the standard valuation tables of Ch. 11, with J replacing t and K replacing f. The qualification is this: the valuation definition for the connective other than $\rightarrow$ which is employed in any particular axiom is modified in a special way for proving the independence of that particular axiom, the nature of the modification, and the values of the variables which give that axiom the value K, being indicated in the following table.

Axiom	*Definition of Connective*	*Value K for*
III	$A \vee B = B$	$p=J,\ q=K$
IV	$A \vee B = A$	$p=K,\ q=J$
V	$A \vee B = J$	$p=q=r=K$
VI	$A \mathbin{\&} B = B$	$p=K,\ q=J$
VII	$A \mathbin{\&} B = A$	$p=J,\ q=K$
VIII	$A \mathbin{\&} B = K$	$p=q=r=J$
IX	$\bar{A} = A$	$p=K,\ q=J$
X	$\bar{A} = K$	$p=J$
XI	$\bar{A} = J$	$p=K$

For example, if the value of $\bar{A}$ is defined to be the value of A itself, the valuation definitions of the other connectives being as in the standard valuation tables (with J for t and K for f), then, when $p=K$ and $q=J$, axiom IX has the value K; for

(3) $(K \to J) \to (\bar{J} \to \bar{K}) = (K \to J) \to (J \to K) = J \to K = K.$
With this valuation definition of the negation sign–none of the other axioms can have the value K.

The independence of axioms I and II is much more difficult to establish than that of axioms III–XI, because the propositional variables must be allowed to have more than two values. The set-up for proving the independence of axiom I involves the variables having four values, while that for proving the independence of axiom II involves the variables having three values.

Firstly, we lay down some valuation definitions which will be used in proving the independence of axioms I and II; these definitions need to be supplemented to cover all possibilities, but the supplementations required for the case of axiom I are different from those required for the case of axiom II, so the supplementations will be given separately.

$$p \to p = p \to J = K \to p = J \quad J \to K = K$$
$$p \vee p = p \vee K = p \quad p \vee q = q \vee p \quad p \vee J = J$$
$$(4) \quad p \,\&\, p = p \,\&\, J = p \quad p \,\&\, q = q \,\&\, p \quad p \,\&\, K = K$$
$$\bar{J} = K \quad \bar{K} = J.$$

Next, we concentrate on proving the independence of axiom I. For this, we regard propositional variables as variables having the four possible values J, K, L, and M. The valuation definitions of the connectives are given by (4) supplemented by

$$J \to L = J \to M = L \to K = L \to M = M \to K = K \quad M \to L = J$$
$$(5) \quad L \vee M = L$$
$$L \,\&\, M = M$$
$$\bar{L} = M \quad \bar{M} = L.$$

Axiom I has the value K when $p = M$ and $q = J$, for, by (5), $M \to (J \to M) = M \to K = K$. It can be shown, though it is laborious to do so, that every other axiom always has the value J. It can also be shown that if a formula

A is deduced by substitution or *modus ponens* from J-formulae, then A too is a J-formula. Hence, axiom I cannot be deduced from the other axioms.

Let us turn to the case of axiom II. We regard propositional variables as variables having three possible values J, K, and L. The valuation definitions of the connectives are given by (4) supplemented by

(6) $J \to L = L \to K = L$
$\bar{L} = L.$

Axiom II has the value L when $p = q = L$ and $r = K$, for, by (4) and (6),

(7) $(L \to (L \to K)) \to ((L \to L) \to (L \to K)) =$
$(L \to L) \to (J \to L) = J \to L = L.$

It can be shown that every other axiom always has the value J. It can also be shown that if a formula A is deduced by substitution or *modus ponens* from J-formulae, then A too is a J-formula. Hence, axiom II cannot be deduced from the other axioms.

In view of the material presented in this section we are entitled to assert

Theorem 46. None of the axioms of P can be deduced from the remaining axioms by use of the rule of substitution or the rule of *modus ponens*.

Finally, it might be asked whether the two rules of substitution and *modus ponens* of P are independent of one another. Without making any pretence at rigour, we can say that each rule contributes essentially to what is provable in P, so that neither is redundant. If the rule of substitution were eliminated, it would be impossible to deduce from the axioms a formula such as

(8) $(p \to q) \to ((r \to s) \to (p \,\&\, r \to q \,\&\, s)),$

(cf. Ch. 10, (17)), for the letter s does not occur in any axiom and obviously *modus ponens* does not alter constituent propositional variables of formulae. And if the rule of *modus ponens* were eliminated, it would be impossible to deduce from the axioms a formula such as $p \rightarrow p$ or $p \vee \bar{p}$, for none of the axioms are of these forms and substitution can alter only the details but not the outline structure of a formula.

Chapter Thirteen

COMPLETENESS

A system of the propositional calculus in which every t-formula (relatively to the standard valuation tables of Ch. 11) is provable is called *complete*. Our system P is complete, as we shall now proceed to prove.

Theorem 47. $(p \sim V) \sim p$ is provable.

Proof: 1. $p \sim V°$
*2. $V \to p$
3. V
4. p

In this deduction, 2 comes from 1 by virtue of axiom VII, 3 is provable (by notational definition), and 4 is 2, 3, mp. This deduction shows that

(1) $p \sim V \vdash p$.

1. $p°$
2. $p \to V$
3. $p \to (q \to p)$
4. $p \to (V \to p)$
5. $V \to p$
6. $p \to (q \to p \;\&\; q)$
*7. $(p \to V) \to ((V \to p) \to (p \sim V))$
*8. $p \sim V$.

In this deduction, 2 is Ch. 4, Theorem 1, 3 is axiom I, 4 is $S_q^V(3)$, 5 is 1, 4, mp, 6 is Ch. 8, Theorem 15, 7 comes from 6 by substitution, and 8 comes from 2, 5, and 7 by *modus ponens*. This deduction shows that

(2) $p \vdash p \sim V$.

Applying the deduction theorem to (1) and (2) and using Ch. 8, Theorem 15 gives

(3) $\vdash (p \sim V) \sim p$.

Theorem 48. $(p \sim \bar{V}) \sim \bar{p}$ is provable.

Proof:
1. $p \sim \bar{V}^{\circ}$
*2. $p \rightarrow \bar{V}$
3. $(p \rightarrow \bar{q}) \rightarrow (q \rightarrow \bar{p})$
4. $(p \rightarrow \bar{V}) \rightarrow (V \rightarrow \bar{p})$
5. $V \rightarrow \bar{p}$
6. V
7. $\bar{p}$.

In this deduction, 2 comes from 1 by virtue of axiom VI, 3 is Ch. 8, Theorem 24, 4 is $S^{V}_{q}(3)$, 5 is 2, 4, mp, 6 is provable, 7 is 5, 6, mp. This deduction shows that

(4) $p \sim \bar{V} \vdash \bar{p}$.

1. $\bar{p}^{\circ}$
2. $p \rightarrow (\bar{p} \rightarrow \bar{V})$
3. $(p \rightarrow (q \rightarrow r)) \rightarrow (q \rightarrow (p \rightarrow r))$
*4. $(p \rightarrow (\bar{p} \rightarrow \bar{V})) \rightarrow (\bar{p} \rightarrow (p \rightarrow \bar{V}))$
5. $\bar{p} \rightarrow (p \rightarrow \bar{V})$
6. $p \rightarrow \bar{V}$
7. $\bar{V} \rightarrow p$
*8. $p \sim \bar{V}$.

In this deduction, 2 is step 13 in the proof of Ch. 4, Theorem 13, 3 is Ch. 8, Theorem 20, 4 comes from 3 by substitution, 5 is 2, 4, mp, 6 is 1, 5, mp, 7 is Ch. 4, Theorem 12, and 8 comes by substituting 6 and 7 in

Ch. 8, Theorem 15 and using *modus ponens*. This deduction shows that

(5) $\bar{p} \vdash p \sim \bar{V}$.

Applying the deduction theorem to (4) and (5) and using Ch. 8, Theorem 15 gives

(6) $\vdash (p \sim \bar{V}) \sim \bar{p}$.

Theorem 49. $(p \sim V) \vee (p \sim \bar{V})$ is provable.

Proof: By Theorem 47,

(7) $p \vee \bar{p}, p \vdash p \sim V$;

since, by axiom III, $(p \sim V) \rightarrow (p \sim V) \vee (p \sim \bar{V})$,

(8) $p \vee \bar{p}, p \vdash (p \sim V) \vee (p \sim \bar{V})$.

By Theorem 48,

(9) $p \vee \bar{p}, \bar{p} \vdash p \sim \bar{V}$;

since, by axiom IV, $(p \sim \bar{V}) \rightarrow (p \sim V) \vee (p \sim \bar{V})$,

(10) $p \vee \bar{p}, \bar{p} \vdash (p \sim V) \vee (p \sim \bar{V})$.

By Ch. 9, Lemma 5 applied to (8) and (10),

(11) $p \vee \bar{p} \vdash (p \sim V) \vee (p \sim \bar{V})$.

Hence, by Ch. 4, Theorem 13,

(12) $\vdash (p \sim V) \vee (p \sim \bar{V})$.

Theorem 50. [If $A(D)$ is a formula containing any propositional variable D, then]

(13) $A(V) \& A(\bar{V}) \rightarrow ((p \sim V) \rightarrow A(p)) \& ((p \sim \bar{V}) \rightarrow A(p))$ is provable.

Proof: One formulation of Ch. 10, Theorem 38 is that if D is a propositional variable that occurs in A, then

(14) $(B \sim C) \rightarrow (A(B) \sim A(C))$ is provable.

This formulation is justified by the proof of Theorem 38 together with the deduction theorem.

Let E be a propositional variable that does not occur in $A(p)$.

$$
\begin{array}{rl}
1. & (p \sim E) \rightarrow (A(p) \sim A(E)) \\
*2. & (A(p) \sim A(E)) \rightarrow (A(E) \rightarrow A(p)) \\
3. & (p \sim E) \rightarrow (A(E) \rightarrow A(p)) \\
4. & (p \rightarrow (q \rightarrow r)) \rightarrow (q \rightarrow (p \rightarrow r)) \\
*5. & A(E) \rightarrow ((p \sim E) \rightarrow A(p)) \\
6. & A(V) \rightarrow ((p \sim V) \rightarrow A(p)) \\
*7. & A(V) \,\&\, A(\overline{V}) \rightarrow A(V) \\
8. & A(V) \,\&\, A(\overline{V}) \rightarrow ((p \sim V) \rightarrow A(p)) \\
9. & A(\overline{V}) \rightarrow ((p \sim \overline{V}) \rightarrow A(p)) \\
*10. & A(V) \,\&\, A(\overline{V}) \rightarrow A(\overline{V}) \\
11. & A(V) \,\&\, A(\overline{V}) \rightarrow ((p \sim \overline{V}) \rightarrow A(p)) \\
12. & (r \rightarrow p) \rightarrow ((r \rightarrow q) \rightarrow (r \rightarrow p \,\&\, q)) \\
*13. & A(V) \,\&\, A(\overline{V}) \rightarrow ((p \sim V) \rightarrow A(p)) \,\&\, \\
 & \qquad ((p \sim \overline{V}) \rightarrow A(p)).
\end{array}
$$

In this deduction, 1 is justified by Ch. 10, Theorem 38 (cf. (14) above), 2 is justified by axiom VII, 3 is 1, 2, syll, 4 is Ch. 8, Theorem 20, 5 comes from applying 4 to 3, 6 is $S^{V}_{E}(5)$, 7 is justified by axiom VI, 8 is 6, 7, syll, 9 is $S^{\overline{V}}_{E}(5)$, 10 is justified by axiom VII, 11 is 9, 10, syll, 12 is axiom VIII, and 13 comes from substitution in 12 and from *modus ponens*, using 8 and 11.

Theorem 51. $((p \sim V) \rightarrow A(p)) \,\&\, ((p \sim \overline{V}) \rightarrow A(p)) \rightarrow ((p \sim V) \vee (p \sim \overline{V}) \rightarrow A(p))$ is provable.

Proof: By virtue of axiom V it is true that

(15) $((p \sim V) \rightarrow A(p)) \,\&\, ((p \sim \overline{V}) \rightarrow A(p)) \vdash (p \sim V) \vee (p \sim \overline{V}) \rightarrow A(p)$.

Applying the deduction theorem to (15) gives the theorem.

Theorem 52. $A(V)$ & $A(\overline{V}) \rightarrow ((p \sim V) \vee (p \sim \overline{V}) \rightarrow A(p))$ is provable.

Proof: The theorem is obtainable by applying the syllogistic principle to Theorems 50 and 51.

Theorem 53. $A(V)$ & $A(\overline{V}) \rightarrow A(p)$ is provable.

Proof: By Ch. 8, Theorem 20 it follows from Theorem 52 that

(16) $(p \sim V) \vee (p \sim \overline{V}) \rightarrow A(V)$ & $A(\overline{V}) \rightarrow A(p))$ is provable.

Since the antecedent in the formula in (16) is provable, by Theorem 49, the truth of the theorem follows, by *modus ponens*.

Considering an example, let A be

(17) $(r \rightarrow p$ & $q) \vee \bar{r}$,

and let us interest ourselves in the variable r. By Theorem 53,

(18) $\vdash ((V \rightarrow p$ & $q) \vee \overline{V})$ & $((\overline{V} \rightarrow p$ & $q) \vee \overline{\overline{V}}) \rightarrow (r \rightarrow p$ & $q) \vee \bar{r}$.

To indicate the propositional variables A contains, (17) can be expressed briefly as $A(p, q, r)$ and (18) can then be put in the form

(19) $\vdash A(p, q, V)$ & $A(p, q, \overline{V}) \rightarrow A(p, q, r)$.

Next, suppose a formula A contains at least one occurrence of each of the distinct propositional variables $D_1, D_2, \ldots, D_n$ and contains no occurrence of any other propositional variable. If we wish to make explicit the propositional variables contained in A we may write A as $A(D_1, D_2, \ldots, D_n)$. If A is $A(D_1, D_2)$, then *e.g.* $A(V, \overline{V})$ denotes the formula that is the same as A except that each occurrence of D_1 and of D_2 has become an occurrence of V and of $\overline{V}$ respectively; for example, if $A(p, q)$ is $q \to p \vee \bar{q}$, then $A(V, \bar{V})$ is $\bar{V} \to V \vee \bar{\bar{V}}$.

It is convenient to have a brief notation for

(20) $A(V)$ & $A(\bar{V})$ [when A contains only one propositional variable],

for

(21) $A(V, V)$ & $A(V, \bar{V})$ & $A(\bar{V}, V)$ & $A(\bar{V}, \bar{V})$ [when A contains exactly two propositional variables],

for

(22) $A(V, V, V)$ & $A(V, V, \bar{V})$ & $A(V, \bar{V}, V)$ & $A(V, \bar{V}, \bar{V})$ & $A(\bar{V}, V, V)$ & $A(\bar{V}, V, \bar{V})$ & $A(\bar{V}, \bar{V}, V)$ & $A(\bar{V}, \bar{V}, \bar{V})$ [when A contains exactly three propositional variables],

and so on. The notation used is

(23) $\Pi\ A(\epsilon_1, \epsilon_2, \ldots, \epsilon_n)$, $\qquad \epsilon_i = V, \bar{V}$.

By definition, $\Pi\ A(\epsilon_1)=(20)$, $\Pi\ A(\epsilon_1, \epsilon_2)=(21)$, $\Pi\ A(\epsilon_1, \epsilon_2, \epsilon_3)=(22)$, and so on. A general definition of (23) is: if $n=1$,

(24) $\Pi\ A(\epsilon_1, \epsilon_2, \ldots, \epsilon_n)=A(V)$ & $A(\bar{V})$;

if (23) has been defined for each $n \leq m$, then

(25) $\Pi\ A(\epsilon_1, \epsilon_2, \ldots, \epsilon_{m+1})=\Pi\ A(\epsilon_1, \epsilon_2, \ldots, \epsilon_m, V)$ & $\Pi\ A(\epsilon_1, \epsilon_2, \ldots, \epsilon_m, \bar{V})$.

Theorem 54. $\Pi\ A(\epsilon_1, \epsilon_2, \ldots, \epsilon_n) \to A(D_1, D_2, \ldots, D_n)$ is provable.

Proof: First, let us consider the case when $n=1$. Then the theorem says that $\Pi\ A(\epsilon_1) \to A(D_1)$ is provable; this is true, by Theorem 53. Assuming the truth of the theorem for each $k \leq m$, let us derive as a consequence the truth of

(26) $\vdash \Pi\ A(\epsilon_1, \epsilon_2, \ldots, \epsilon_{m+1}) \rightarrow A(D_1, D_2, \ldots, D_{m+1})$.
By definition,

(27) $\Pi\ A(\epsilon_1, \epsilon_2, \ldots, \epsilon_{m+1}) = \Pi\ A(\epsilon_1, \epsilon_2, \ldots, \epsilon_m, V)\ \&$
$\Pi\ A(\epsilon_1, \epsilon_2, \ldots, \epsilon_m, \overline{V})$.

By $T(k \leq m)$, which is being assumed as true,

(28) $\vdash \Pi\ A(\epsilon_1, \epsilon_2, \ldots, \epsilon_m, V) \rightarrow A(D_1, D_2, \ldots, D_m, V)$

and

(29) $\vdash \Pi\ A(\epsilon_1, \epsilon_2, \ldots, \epsilon_m, \overline{V}) \rightarrow A(D_1, D_2, \ldots, D_m, \overline{V})$.

Therefore, by Ch. 10 (17),

(30) $\vdash \Pi\ A(\epsilon_1, \epsilon_2, \ldots, \epsilon_{m+1}) \rightarrow A(D_1, D_2, \ldots, D_m, V)$
$\&\ A(D_1, D_2, \ldots, D_m, \overline{V})$.

(26) now follows by Theorem 53. This establishes the theorem.

If the propositional variables contained in a formula A are replaced by V or $\overline{V}$, each occurrence of the same variable being replaced in the same way with occurrences of different variables possibly being replaced differently, then the resulting formula is denoted by $A[V, \overline{V}]$.

Theorem 55. If the propositional variables of A are replaced by V or $\overline{V}$, and if the propositional variables may have the values t and f, then if t is the value given to those propositional variables which are replaced by V and f is the value given to those which are replaced by $\overline{V}$, then: if the value of A itself is t, $A[V, \overline{V}]$ is equivalent to V, while if the value of A itself is f, $A[V, \overline{V}]$ is equivalent to $\overline{V}$. (The standard valuation tables are assumed.)

Proof: We shall show first that the theorem is true for the case when A contains no occurrences of connectives, that is when A is a propositional variable D. If D is replaced by V, then, by the prescribed conditions. A

must have the value t; since $A[V, \overline{V}]$ is V, it is true that $\vdash A[V, \overline{V}] \sim V$. If D is replaced by $\overline{V}$, then A must have the value f; since $A[V, \overline{V}]$ is $\overline{V}$, it is true that $\vdash A[V, \overline{V}] \sim \overline{V}$. Thus, in the notation of Ch. 6, $T(0)$ is true.

We now suppose that $T(k \leq m)$ is true and attempt to derive as a consequence the truth of $T(m+1)$, that is that the theorem is true for any formula A which contains $m+1$ occurrences of connectives. If a formula A has $m+1$ occurrences of connectives, the principal connective is either (*a*) $-$, (*b*) $\vee$, (*c*) &, or (*d*) $\rightarrow$.

(*a*) If A is of the form $\overline{B}$, then, when A has the value t, B must have the value f (by the standard valuation table for negation). By $T(k \leq m)$, $\vdash B[V, \overline{V}] \sim \overline{V}$; therefore, $\vdash \overline{B}[V, \overline{V}] \sim \overline{\overline{V}}$, by the proof on page 51, and hence, by Ch. 10, Theorems 34 and 37, $\vdash A[V, \overline{V}] \sim V$. When A has the value f, B has the value t. By $T(k \leq m)$, $\vdash B[V, \overline{V}] \sim V$; therefore, $\vdash \overline{B}[V, \overline{V}] \sim \overline{V}$, again by the proof on page 51; so $\vdash A[V, \overline{V}] \sim \overline{V}$.

(*b*) If A is of the form $B \vee C$, then, when A has the value f, B and C must have the value f (by the standard valuation table for disjunction). By $T(k \leq m)$, $\vdash B[V, \overline{V}] \sim \overline{V}$ and $\vdash C[V, \overline{V}] \sim \overline{V}$; therefore,

(31) $\vdash (B[V, \overline{V}] \vee [CV, \overline{V}]) \sim (\overline{V} \vee \overline{V})$,

by the proof on page 54. By Ch. 4, Theorems 5 and 7,

(32) $\vdash [\overline{V} \vee \overline{V}] \sim \overline{V}$.

It follows from (31), (32), and Ch. 10, Theorem 37 that $\vdash A[V, \overline{V}] \sim \overline{V}$. When A has the value t, either B and C have the value t or just one of B and C has this value. We shall deal with the case when B has the value t and C has the value f, leaving the other two cases to the reader. If B has the value t and C has the value f, then, by $T(k \leq m)$, $\vdash B[V, \overline{V}] \sim V$ and $\vdash C[V, \overline{V}] \sim \overline{V}$; hence by the proof on page 54,

(33) $\vdash (B[V, \overline{V}] \vee C[V, \overline{V}]) \sim (V \vee \overline{V})$,

that is $\vdash A[V, \overline{V}] \sim (V \vee \overline{V})$. By the definition of $\vdash$,

(34) $V \vee \overline{V}, V \vdash V$;

also, by Ch. 4, Theorem 12,

(35) $V \vee \overline{V}, \overline{V} \vdash V$.

From (34) and (35) and axiom III, it follows that

(36) $\vdash (V \vee \overline{V}) \sim V$.

Therefore, $\vdash A[V, \overline{V}] \sim V$.

(*c*) If A is of the form B & C, then, when A has the value t, B and C have that value (by the standard valuation table for conjunction). By $T(k \leq m)$, $\vdash B[V, \overline{V}] \sim V$ and $\vdash C[V, \overline{V}] \sim V$; hence, by the proof on pages 56–7,

(37) $\vdash (B[V, \overline{V}] \;\&\; C[V, \overline{V}]) \sim (V \;\&\; V)$,

that is $\vdash A[V, \overline{V}] \sim (V \;\&\; V)$. By Ch. 4, Theorems 6 and 8,

(38) $\vdash (V \;\&\; V) \sim V$.

Therefore, $\vdash A[V, \overline{V}] \sim V$. When A has the value f, either B and C have that value or just one of B and C has it. We shall deal with the case when B has the value f and C has the value t, leaving the other two cases to the reader. If B has the value f and C has the value t, then, by $T(k \leq m)$, $\vdash B[V, \overline{V}] \sim \overline{V}$ and $C[V, \overline{V}] \sim V$; hence, by the proof on pages 56–7,

(39) $\vdash (B[V, \overline{V}] \;\&\; C[V, \overline{V}]) \sim (\overline{V} \;\&\; V)$,

that is $\vdash A[V, V] \sim (V \;\&\; \overline{V})$. It follows from axiom VI and Ch. 4, Theorem 12 that

(40) $\vdash (\overline{V} \;\&\; V) \sim \overline{V}$.

Therefore, $\vdash A[V, \overline{V}] \sim \overline{V}$.

(*d*) If A is of the form $B \rightarrow C$, then, when A has the value f, B has the value t and C has the value f (by the standard valuation table for implication). By $\vdash(k \leq m)$, $\vdash B[V, \overline{V}] \sim V$ and $\vdash C[V, \overline{V}] \sim \overline{V}$; hence, by Ch. 10 (27),

(41) $\vdash(B[V, \overline{V}] \rightarrow C[V, \overline{V}]) \sim (V \rightarrow \overline{V})$,

that is $\vdash A[V, \overline{V}] \sim (V \rightarrow \overline{V})$.

(42) $\vdash(V \rightarrow \overline{V}) \rightarrow \overline{V}$,

for, by *modus ponens* and the fact that $\vdash V$, it follows that $V \rightarrow \overline{V}$ yields $\overline{V}$; also, by axiom I,

(43) $\vdash \overline{V} \rightarrow (V \rightarrow \overline{V})$.

From (42) and (43) it follows that

(44) $\vdash(V \rightarrow \overline{V}) \sim \overline{V}$.

Therefore, $\vdash A[V, \overline{V}] \sim \overline{V}$. When A has the value t, either B and C have that value or B has the value f (C having the value t or the value f). We shall deal with the case when B and C have the value f, leaving the other two cases to the reader. If B and C have the value f, then, by $T(k \leq m)$, $\vdash B[V, \overline{V}] \sim \overline{V}$ and $\vdash C\,[V, \overline{V}] \sim \overline{V}$; hence, by Ch. 10 (27),

(45) $\vdash(B[V, \overline{V}] \rightarrow C[V, \overline{V}]) \sim (\overline{V} \rightarrow \overline{V})$,

that is $\vdash A[V, \overline{V}] \sim (\overline{V} \rightarrow \overline{V})$. By Ch. 4, Theorem 2 and Ch. 10, Theorem 36,

(46) $\vdash(\overline{V} \rightarrow \overline{V}) \sim V$.

Therefore, $\vdash A[V, \overline{V}] \sim V$.

Theorem 56. Every t-formula is provable.

Proof: If $A(D_1, D_2, \ldots, D_n)$ is a t-formula ($n \geq 1$), then, by Theorem 55, $\vdash A[V, \overline{V}] \sim V$ for every possible replacement of the propositional variables D_i by V or $\overline{V}$. Since V is provable, each $A[V, \overline{V}]$ is provable, so that

(47) $\Pi\ A(\epsilon_1, \epsilon_2, \ldots, \epsilon_n)$ is provable.

It follows from (47) and Theorem 54, by *modus ponens*, that $A(D_1, D_2, \ldots, D_n)$ is provable.

A consistent system which is such that, if a non-provable formula were added to the body of provable formulae of the system, then the extended system would not be consistent, is called *saturated* or *absolutely complete*. When this notion of completeness is being considered, the type of completeness we have been establishing for P is called *relative* completeness.

Theorem 57. P is absolutely complete.

Proof: By Theorem 56, if $A(D_1, D_2, \ldots, D_n)$ is a non-provable formula, it is not a t-formula. Therefore, A has the value f for some assignment of values to its propositional variables D_i. Replacing each D_i that has the value t, or f, in such an assignment, by V, or $\overline{V}$, respectively, the formula $A[V, \overline{V}]$ that results is equivalent to $\overline{V}$, by Theorem 55. If A were allowed to be provable, it would follow, by use of the rule of substitution, that $A[V, \overline{V}]$ would be provable. Since this formula is equivalent to $\overline{V}$, any pair of contradictory formulae would become provable, by Ch. 4, Theorem 12.

BIBLIOGRAPHY

Suitable works for following up the material presented in this Monograph are:

1. LORENZEN, P., *Formal Logic*, 1962 (translation of *Formale Logik*, 1958), Chapters I–IV.

2. SCHÜTTE, K., *Beweistheorie*, 1960, Parts I–II.

3. SUPPES, P., *Introduction to Logic*, 1957, Chapters 1–2.

The reader interested in minutely detailed accounts of Propositional Calculi, either for study or for reference, should consult:

4. CHURCH, A., *Introduction to Mathematical Logic*, Volume 1, 1956.

5. SCHMIDT, ARNOLD H., *Mathematische Grundlagen der Logik I—Vorlesungen über Aussagenlogik*, 1960.

INDEX